Wastewater treatment

EVALUATION AND IMPLEMENTATION

WATER ENVIRONMENT SERIES

Wastewater treatment

EVALUATION AND IMPLEMENTATION

*Proceedings of Water Environment '94, a joint
Institution of Civil Engineers and Institution of Water
and Environment Management conference, held in
London on 9 – 10 March 1994*

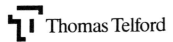

Thomas Telford

Water Environment '94 embraces the Institution of Civil Engineers' World Water conference series and the Institution of Water Management's 1994 Annual Conference

Conference organized by Thomas Telford Services Ltd and IWEM on behalf of the Institution of Civil Engineers and the Institution of Water and Environmental Management

Organizing Committee:
B. H. Rofe, Rofe Kennard & Lapworth (Chairman);
J. Bircumshaw, Institution of Civil Engineers and Southern Water Services Ltd;
K. F. Clarke, Institution of Water & Environmental Management;
H. M. Ferguson, Thomas Telford Services Ltd;
L. Gittins, Institution of Water & Environmental Management;
K. Hayward, Water and Environment Management Magazine;
J. R. Martin, Severn Trent Water Ltd;
T. H. Y. Tebbutt, Biwater Ltd *1092 1699*

First published 1994

A CIP catalogue record for this publication is available from the British Library.

ISBN 0 7277 1991 2

Classification
Availability: unrestricted
Content: collected papers
Status: refereed
User: water and environment engineers, scientists and planners

Published by Thomas Telford Services Ltd, Thomas Telford House, 1 Heron Quay, London E14 4JD.

Printed and bound in Great Britain by The Cromwell Press, Melksham, Wilts.

Contents

Implications of wastewater directives and regulation from a water company perspective

B. A. O. HEWETT, BSc(Eng), MSc, FICE, FIWEM, FIMgt, Director of
Technical and Environmental Affairs, South West Water Plc, Exeter,
B. J. MOORHOUSE, MA (Oxon), FCMA, Regulatory Director, and
R. J. BATY, CEng, FICE, FIWEM, MIMgt, ACIArb, Engineering Director,
South West Water Services Ltd, Exeter

SYNOPSIS

South West Water is faced with delivering major environmental
improvements in response to the demands of UK and EC legislation. On
marine effluent treatment alone this requires expenditure of £900 million
over the period 1989-2000. The Company seeks to balance the demands
for environmental improvements against two other major factors, namely
the cost and the affordability of the overall capital programme.
Furthermore, innovative engineering solutions are crucial to the
Company's success in delivering the results.

INTRODUCTION

1. South West Water, like many other water service companies, is faced
with delivering major environmental improvements in response to the
demands of UK and EC policy and legislation governing waste water
treatment and disposal. At the same time, the Company is keen to satisfy
the demands and aspirations of its customers and shareholders. This
requires a careful balancing act to satisfy all key stakeholders. This paper
examines key elements of this balance and explores some examples of
innovative solutions provided by the Company.

  2. Four key themes will be emphasised:-
- (a) Environmental Benefit,
- (b) Cost,
- (c) Affordability,
- (d) Innovative Engineering.

The first three form elements of a conceptual triangle, shown in Fig. 1.
This illustrates the nature of the challenge facing the Company in seeking
to deliver optimal waste water solutions. The final theme examines the
innovative approach to engineering solutions adopted by South West Water
in delivering schemes, once the right balance has been struck. Each theme
will be explored in turn.

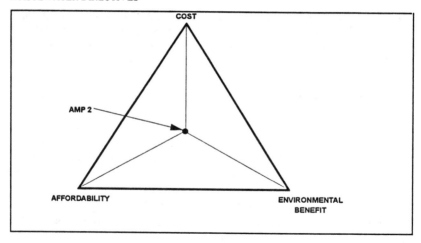

Fig. 1. Key themes

ENVIRONMENTAL BENEFIT

3. The achievement of environmental benefit in waste water terms is judged against a combination of EC and UK legislative requirements, the main elements of which are depicted in Fig. 2. EC Directives are firmly based upon the notion of emission standards and the provision of best available technology. These requirements are superimposed on a further set of UK policy and legislative measures designed to achieve environmental quality objectives. Both sets of considerations act as investment drivers, influencing cost and practical engineering decisions.

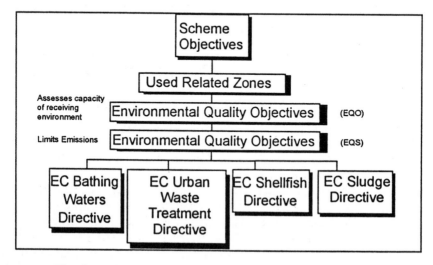

Fig. 2. EC and UK waste legislation

4. Numerous papers have reviewed the requirements and implications of UK and EC environmental legislation, especially the Urban Waste Water Treatment Directive, (Ref. 1, 2, 3, 4, 5, 6, 7, 8, 9). The above give a good flavour of its content and its wide ranging effects on process engineering decisions. Similarly, key elements of UK legislation such as the establishment of Statutory Water Quality Objectives have been well covered (Ref. 10 and 11).

5. Selected elements of the EC Urban Waste Water Treatment Directive serve as a good illustration of the wide range of waste water treatment required from South West Water, dependent upon the location, size and potential impact of a discharge, as shown in Fig. 3. Hence, discharges of varying sizes to inland, estuarine and coastal waters can require a variety of treatment levels, which in many cases for small discharges will be dependent upon the quality regulator's interpretation of what constitutes "appropriate treatment".

POPULATION EQUIVALENT		<250	250 to 2,000	2,000 to 10000	10,000 to 15,000	15,000 to 150,000	>150,000
WATER							
FRESHWATER	Normal	A/B	B/A	C	C	C	C
	Sensitive				.Cx	Cx	Cx
ESTUARIES	Less Sensitive			D			
	Normal	A/B	B/A	C	C	C	C
	Sensitive				Cx	Cx	Cx
COASTAL	Less Sensitive				D	D	
	Normal	A	B/A	B/A	C	C	C
	Sensitive				Cx	Cx	Cx

A = Appropriate treatment descriptive
B = Appropriate treatment numeric
C = Secondary treatment
Cx = "More Stringent" treatment and secondary unless approved otherwise under Annex 1A
D = Primary Treatment
☐ = Less Sensitive/Sensitive is not an option

Fig. 3.   Urban waste water treatment directive treatment options

6. Similarly, UK environmental policy and legislation often seeks further effluent design standards to protect, for example, fisheries eco-systems through appropriate levels of nitrification; or in the case of marine discharges, the achievement of initial dilution as a means of protecting bathing water appearance.

7. Taken together, these complementary requirements must be managed by the company within the context of overall waste water scheme objectives. The entire process entails extensive consultation with the quality regulators, primarily the NRA, planning authorities and our customers, on the technical and environmental aspects of the Company's proposals and ultimately its preferred scheme. Detailed scheme appraisal in conjunction with NRA is therefore accompanied by an environmental

assessment and a carefully thought out scheme promotion, emphasising the environmental benefits being provided by the Company at each specific location.

8. Clearly, the environmental benefits sought from any waste water investments are the subject of a complex balance of legislative demands and environmental need. It is the task of South West Water to recognise its statutory obligations and the environmental aspirations of the quality regulators as well as its customers in arriving at a preferred scheme which satisfies all of these demands. At the same time, the Company needs to be mindful of the two other key elements of the decision making process highlighted in Fig. 1, namely cost and affordability.

COST CONSIDERATIONS

9. The cost of providing a massive environmental clean up by the water industry as a whole has been the subject of widespread discussion and examination by the industry's financial and quality regulators in cooperation with all water service companies. The outcome has been widely publicised (Ref. 12 and 13), and has confirmed the significant burden of waste water related investments, linked to both EC and UK statutory obligations. In particular the EC Urban Waste Water Treatment Directive and EC Sludge Directive (Ref. 14 and 15) have been noted as major investment drivers in the period commencing 1 April 1995.

10. South West Water's current commitment to such legal obligations up to the year 2000 is summarised in Fig. 4. As can be seen, our current "Clean Sweep" commitments to clean up 81 EC designated beaches through the implementation of 33 major schemes dominates our projected waste water spend at around £900m. In addition, significant sums of money are also identified for sludge, inland sewerage, and inland sewage treatment. This includes for significant uprating of 140 of the larger sewage treatment works by 1995, located throughout the Company's area. Further improvements to achieve Urban Waste Water Treatment Directive standards are anticipated for systems serving larger agglomerations.

11. Justification for such major capital expenditure needs to be carefully communicated to our customers, identifying the benefits to individual customers and the regional economy. Indeed, our capital spend, totalling £4m per week, has very significant and positive benefits on the local economy, which should not be lost sight of when examining the costs of delivering such environmental benefits.

12. The Company has employed a variety of techniques to communicate these issues to our customers. Preparatory consultation through publication of a "Water - Your Views?" brochure, offering customers the opportunity to comment on current and future expenditure plans was accompanied by extensive customer consultation exercises using a variety of market research techniques. This culminated in the production of our Market Plan, reflecting customer views and indicating the likely cost of

future obligations. Public meetings and "Water Days" were also held to discuss our plans for waste water investment with all interested parties.

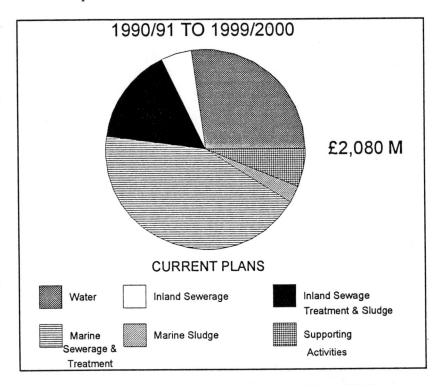

Fig. 4. SWWS current capital programme (1990 - 2000)

13. The cost of the improvements has also been summarised in terms of the likely impact on average water charges by the year 2000. Reductions in charges associated with possible modification of the demands for further environmental improvements were also predicted. Such exercises give visibility to the critical need to balance cost and environmental benefit, a balance which is fundamental to South West Water's business.

14. Given the pressure on costs, the Company is continually examining ways of employing new technology in an innovative manner to deliver the same environmental benefits at reduced costs.

15. The drive to raise standards and keep costs to the minimum has stimulated the development and application of new technologies in all water service companies in England and Wales. In South West Water considerable resources have been devoted since privatisation to research and development in the waste water function, mostly in treatment process technology.

16. Lastly, another fundamental reason for controlling costs relates back to the third and final element of the conceptual model that this paper focuses upon, that of affordability.

AFFORDABILITY

17. South West Water serves a permanent population of 1.5 million, with a paying customer base of around 650,000. This is a critical factor in the size of average domestic bills needed to fund our massive environmental obligations. Indeed, projections prepared for our Market Plan indicate that bills will reach around £350 in real terms by 1997/8, significantly higher than any other water service company (Fig. 5).

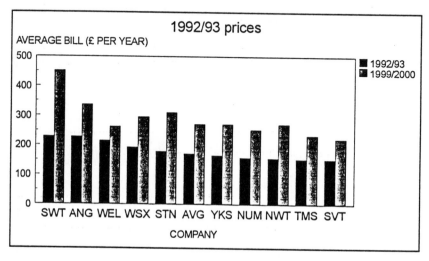

Fig. 5. The implications for customer bills (1992/93 prices)

18. It is not merely the size of bills that determines affordability. Key aspects of the local economy are of critical importance and a number of measures of economic and socio-economic well-being are pertinent.

19. Average earnings and GDP per head of population are two good indicators of the relative wealth of our customer base. The comparison in Figs. 6 and 7 with the equivalent statistics from the other ten water service companies is clear. Many of our customers earn significantly below the national average weekly wage which is similarly reflected in the GDP statistics.

20. The size of current and future water bills means that a larger proportion of disposable income is required from our customers to achieve benefits to the local environment and improvements to the service (Fig. 8). The proportion is also set to grow significantly in the next five years.

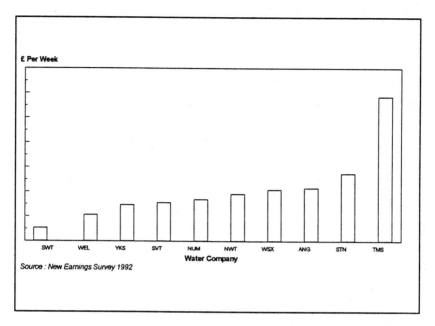

Fig. 6. Affordability : average earnings (1989)

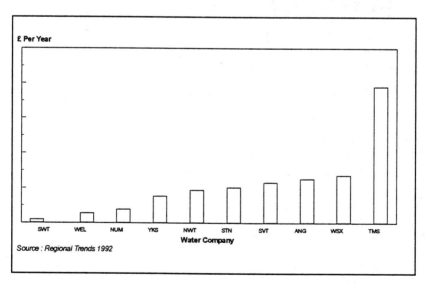

Fig. 7. Affordability : GDP (1989)

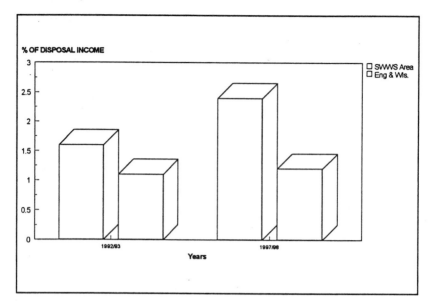

Fig.8. Affordability : water bills as % of disposable income

21. Customers are not all equally affected by the size of water bills.
Well-known vulnerable groups such as single parent families and
pensioners are recognised by the Company, and easy payment facilities are
provided. Again however, the South West is exposed to a greater than
average proportion of pensioner-only households (Fig. 9), which further
highlights customer sensitivity to the issue of affordability.

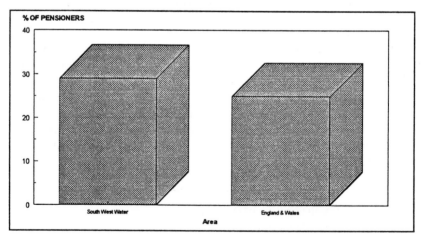

Fig. 9. Affordability : vulnerable groups   (Pensioners)

22. Our customers' ability to fund our legal obligations can be measured by economic indicators. Our customers' willingness to fund improvements can be measured by market research. Both sets of indicators are used by the Company to support management decisions and our future business plans as well as the type of engineering solutions required.

23. One graphic measure of the combined effect of affordability and environmental benefit can be seen in Fig. 10. The ratio of the number of EC beaches per population served for all ten WSCs demonstrates the inordinate burden placed upon 3% of the population of England and Wales in seeking to clean up 30% of EC Bathing Waters.

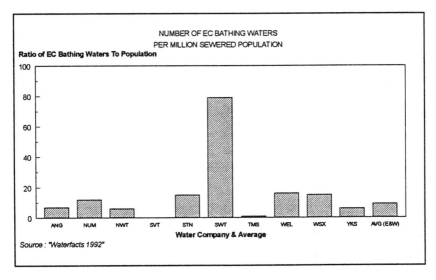

Fig. 10. Affordability : the environmental burden

INNOVATIVE ENGINEERING

24. Numerous case studies exist within published literature describing solutions driven by waste water legislation (Ref. 16 and 17). Rather than examine one or two case studies in detail, this section of the paper concentrates on illustrating the Company's innovative approach to the engineering aspects of solving waste water problems. Some of the innovative solutions incorporated in the Clean Sweep bathing waters improvement programme are described below. Such schemes vary according to:-

    (a)   Size of discharge,
    (b)   Environmental benefits sought,
    (c)   Availability of resources,
    (d)   Customer preference,
    (e)   Site Specifics.

Dartmouth / Kingswear

25. This scheme serves 9500 people, located in a compact community along the Dart Estuary. Nearby EC bathing waters and the estuarine dynamics necessitate secondary treatment, since only limited dilution and dispersion is available prior to the effluent plume reaching the bathing waters. In addition, water sports activity in the estuary requires minimal visual impact from any effluent plume. The major problem was the lack of space for the new works, and hence a compact process solution was devised, utilising lamella plate primary tanks and a biological aerated flooded filter (BAFF) secondary treatment process.

Falmouth

26. Falmouth, serving 43000 people in summer, is another example of limited space for the treatment works. The Company has opted for an innovative aeration technique for the secondary treatment process, using a BAFF. This is to be coupled with a compact settling process to minimise the footprint of the new works. Similar BAFF technology has been used for the Company's Par Scheme, near St Austell in Cornwall, again in order to reduce the plan footprint in a location close to a residential area.

27. Smaller package plant versions, the Copa-BAFF plant, have been developed by one of the Group's subsidiaries. This employs similar technology and is designed to treat populations of around 500 such as the small coastal village of Strete in South Devon.

Ultra Violet Disinfection

28. Taking advantage of the Company's research and development activity in this field, schemes at Porthleven, Salcombe, Lyme Regis and the Camel Estuary, serving populations of 5000, 8000, 11000 and 22000 respectively, are being progressed with the provision of secondary treatment followed by UV disinfection.

29. In the case of Salcombe and the Camel Estuary, the sensitive nature of their respective estuaries for water sports, bathing, recreation and fisheries uses require the production of a very high quality effluent. In addition, the optimum discharge location point is close to these sensitive use areas to maximise the available initial dilution. Hence, the quality of the effluent needs to be approaching that indicated in the EC Bathing Waters Directive prior to its discharge.

Reed Bed Technology

30. Thurlestone and South Milton are served by a single sewage treatment works serving 1200 people in the summer months. This discharges to one of the most environmentally sensitive locations in the country, South Milton Ley, designated an SSSI. Given the requirement to achieve a very tight consent and to substantially reduce nitrate and phosphate loadings to the ley, a reed bed was used to provide tertiary

treatment. Maximum utilisation of the existing assets serving South Milton by refurbishing and extending existing percolating filters was coupled with a new reed bed system in keeping with the nearby natural reed beds. Further downstream the nearby EC Bathing Waters are more than adequately protected by the production of a very high quality effluent (Fig. 11).

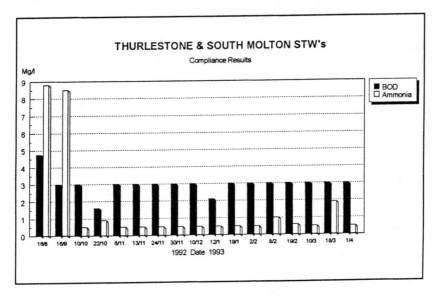

Fig. 11. Reed bed technology performance monitoring

Chemically Assisted Sedimentation

31. This technology has been employed by the Company at Wembury treatment works, utilising the existing primary treatment facilities and sea outfall. Modifications to enable the dosing of ferric sulphate and two polyelectrolytes prior to the effluent entering the primary tanks has enabled the production of a very high quality effluent. Visual impact on the sensitive Marine Conservation Area receiving water has been minimised and there is a major decrease in the effluent's bacteriological content associated with the removal of the majority of the suspended solids and related BOD.

32. Similar technology will be employed at Perranporth, serving 4000 people in winter and 14000 people in summer. A major benefit of such a solution is the flexibility in the treatment process which can be swiftly targeted to the seasonal swings in population experienced in locations like Perranporth. Capital expenditure can be reduced, whilst revenue expenditure is carefully targeted at the peak influent periods of the summer. Such a process is ideally suited to smaller works in an area subjected to a major influx of tourists.

11

Membrane Technology

33. Trials are in hand at Porthilly in Cornwall with a membrane microfiltration system, treating secondary effluent. The advent of this "ultimate barrier" process is regarded by the Company as the most significant technical development in waste water treatment in recent years. Subject to cost considerations, it is likely to be used increasingly by the Company in the years ahead.

CONCLUSION

34. The challenge for South West Water is clear. Environmental benefits have been identified as desirable and are driven by EC and UK waste water legislation and policy. These environmental obligations are regulated through the NRA and its interpretation of the requirements set out in the legislation. South West Water's task is to achieve these environmental benefits at a cost that can be both funded and justified to the satisfaction of our customers, shareholders and financial regulator, OFWAT. At the same time, like any good business, we have to be mindful of the desires, aspirations and ability to pay of our widely diverse customer base. It is a difficult balancing act involving numerous stakeholders, each with different aspirations as to the outcome.

35. Striking this balance requires that the Company remains flexible when offering solutions to a wide range of environmental problems. At the same time, cost and affordability are integral elements of our decision making on a scheme by scheme basis. We have identified no universal panacea to our waste water problems. Each scheme is examined on its merits, mindful of the local environment, the local customers desires and aspirations, and the level of funding. These are the themes and disciplines that guide our approach to meeting the requirements of current waste water directives and regulations.

ACKNOWLEDGEMENT

The authors would like to acknowledge with thanks the assistance of Dr S. C. Bird, Quality Regulation Manager, South West Water Services Ltd., in the preparation of this paper.

REFERENCES

1. SUMMERTON N. Present and Prospective Legislative Trends - What Next? WTi Keynote Seminar, Tadley Court, 8 May 1992.
2. HUNTINGTON R. Implementing the Directive - a Water Company View on Progress. WTi Keynote Seminar, Tadley Court, 8 May 1992.
3. FARRIMOND M. Process Implications of the Directive. WTi Keynote Seminar, Tadley Court, 8 May 1992.
4. HUNTINGTON R. EC Urban Waste Water Treatment Directive - Implication on Sewerage Systems and Sewage Treatment in England and Wales. IWEM Symposium, County Hotel, Taunton, 14 April 1992.

5. HORAN N. J. Background to the Legislation and Implications for Industry. IWEM Symposium, EC Waste Water Treatment Directive - Meeting the Challenges, 1 December 1992, London.

6. TATTERSALL A. S. Waste Water - Considerations of Processes Including Nutrient Removal. IWEM Symposium, EC Waste Water Treatment Directive - Meeting the Challenges, 1 December 1992, London.

7. GREENWOOD B. Implementation of EC Legislation in UK. BICS Conference, Urban Waste Water Treatment - A Review Conference, 28 April 1993, London.

8. CHAVE P. (1993) Implications of Legislation on Water Quality. BICS Conference, Urban Waste Water Treatment - A Review Conference, 28 April 1993, London.

9. HUNTINGTON R., CHAMBERS B. and DEMPSEY P. (1992) Effect of the ECUWWTD on Marine Treatment Practice. J. IWEM, 1992, 6, October.

10. DOE (1992) River Quality : The Government's Proposals (A Consultation Paper). HMSO, December 1992.

11. CHAVE P. (1992) Urban Waste Water Treatment Directive - the NRA's Regulatory Role. WTi Keynote Seminar, Tadley Court, 8 May 1992.

12. OFWAT (1993) The Cost of Quality. OFWAT, 1993, ISBN : 1 874 234 027.

13. OFWAT (1993) Paying for Quality. OFWAT, 1993, ISBN : 1 874 234 06X.

14. MATTHEWS P. (1992) The Urban Waste Water Treatment Directive - Sludge Disposal Concentrations. WTi Keynote Seminar, Tadley Court, 8 May 1992.

15. MATTHEWS P. (1992) Sewage Sludge Disposal in the UK : A New Challenge for the Next Twenty Years. J. IWEM, 1992, 6, October.

16. MIDMER F. (1993) Case Study : The Impact on Coastal Towns. BICS Conference, Urban Waste Water Treatment - A Review Conference, 28 April 1993, London.

17. TRY P. (1993) Case Study. BICS Conference, Urban Waste Water Treatment - A Review Conference, 28 April 1993, London.

Improving the quality of rivers and estuaries

R. J. PENTREATH, BSc, PhD, DSc, Chief Scientist, National Rivers
Authority

SYNOPSIS. The ambit within which improvements to water
quality can be achieved has been the subject of considerable
change; particularly over the last few months. There are a
number of reasons for this, and the medium to long-term
future is still unclear. Thus, in keeping with the new
approach to the setting of EC Directives, this paper is no
more than a brief 'framework' for a discussion on some of
the more substantive issues to be presented at the
Conference in March 1994.

SOME BASIC ASSUMPTIONS
1. It might be thought that setting about the task of
improving the quality of rivers and estuaries was relatively
simple. All one basically needed to decide, for any
particular stretch or body of water was:

(a) what is its current quality;
(b) what is its current use, if any;
(c) what use is required; and
(d) if different, what needs to be done to attain such a
      new water quality state?

2. But such questions instantly raise a number of
subsidiary questions, ranging from the relatively simple

(a) who decides?

to the relatively complicated

(a) what are the benefits;
(b) who benefits;
(c) who suffers if it is not done;
(d) can it be done;
(e) who should pay; and
(f) who would pay?

3. Indeed, the entire discussion can then rapidly extend
to the wider consideration of how pollution prevention and
control practices interface - if at all - with other
fundamental aspects of environmental management within a
"sustainable development" context. Many aspects of
pollution control simply determine what one does not want -
a polluted environment - which is not the same as deciding
what sort of environmental quality one does want, usually

because of the 'use' for which it will be managed, which is normally the case with the freshwater environment.

ASSESSING CURRENT QUALITY

4.   The 'quality' of a stretch of fresh water can vary, depending on the parameter being measured, over periods of minutes, hours, days, months or years. The reason for the variations can be perfectly natural, such as those which affect dissolved oxygen concentrations over a 24 hour cycle, or those due to periods of drought or flood, to those which are due to the discharge or chronic seepage of materials into the water. Equally, the 'quality' of the water can be judged by its chemistry, its biology, or simply its appearance. And for rivers, the 'quality' of the river bank is often as important to the public as the state of the water itself, as judged by parameters invisible to the human eye.

5.   So what is 'water quality'? Can it, in any meaningful way, be assessed for the purposes of sensible management? The NRA's answer to this has been to devise a scheme whereby, given limited and fixed conditions of sampling, all rivers and canals could be chemically assessed in their daylight states for three basic parameters:

(a)   biochemical oxygen demand;
(b)   ammonia; and
(c)   dissolved oxygen.

6.   Using some six 'bands' of values in a classification scheme, and a 'percentile' based system of demonstrating compliance by a minimum sampling regime in space and time, significant changes over periods of a year or more can be demonstrated. But this is a very narrow view of water quality and it is proposed that additional 'windows' be provided to build up a more useful picture. At least one, possibly more, 'biological' windows are needed, plus others to assess factors which may drive changes in biology - such as dissolved nutrients - or even others relating to the aesthetic quality of the river corridor, if it can be sensibly evaluated. But it is then all too easy to devise a list which becomes impossible to deliver - technically or cost-effectively. For estuaries a meaningful and deliverable scheme to enable a general quality assessment to be made is even more difficult. As yet, such a scheme does not exist.

7.   All of these 'windows', however, do not of themselves provide a means of determining what use could be made of a particular stretch of water, nor provide the data necessary for its management. Their purpose is to provide a regular - but not necessarily frequent - overall assessment to enable long-term planning to be made.

SETTING ONE'S SIGHTS

8.   In order to positively manage water quality, it is helpful to consider what its intended 'uses' are, even if it is simply one of being that of water in a river, as generally understood by the public, containing riverine fauna and flora in their natural state. Such 'uses' identified for freshwater management in England and Wales,

for which individual 'standards' could apply in order to assess the extent of achievement of the 'use', are those of:

(a) abstraction – for drinking
                  – for industry, and for agriculture;
(b) water sports; and
(c) commercial harvesting of fish or shellfish.

9. These are hardly surprising. But two others are equally important:

(a) a 'natural river use', termed fisheries ecosystem; and
(b) a special ecosystem use, to protect sites with 'special' ecosystem needs.

10. To some extent, therefore, these are not substantially different from some of the EC framework Directives which are due to emerge (incorporating revisions of some long-established Directives):

(a) freshwater management;
(b) ecological quality of surface water; and
(c) bathing water quality.

11. The setting of such use objectives has to be done at a national level, in a formal way. They serve as goal posts, as landmarks towards achieving a state of sustainable development; they may be difficult and expensive to achieve; they may need defending against other development pressures. If large sums of money are required to achieve them, it is essential for the investors to be assured that the goalposts will not be shifted in the short term. The regulators need the same assurance if their work is to be effective. Such objectives thus also need standards which relate specifically to them.

12. Deriving meaningful yet readily demonstrable compliance standards to be achieved for such uses is not an easy task. Biological ones are difficult in the extreme. But the most difficult legislative task is that of ensuring that other management 'tools' interface in a compatible way with these environmental quality standards.

INTERFACING WITH POLLUTION PREVENTION AND CONTROL
13. A number of EC pollution control Directives have also emerged, or are emerging, in a 'framework' style:

(a) control of dangerous substances;
(b) urban waste water treatment;
(c) nitrates; and
(d) integrated pollution prevention and control.

14. A variety of national legislation also relates to pollution control. If such legislation is not to result in expenditure which results in no clear environmental benefit, other than having 'less of' a substance free in the environment – which can be a perfectly acceptable reason – then it needs to be linked to the more positive environmental standards relating to environmental 'use'. Thus, in interfacing integrated pollution control with freshwaters, the 'use' related standards can and do provide

a boundary for assessing the best practicable environmental option for a particular waste disposal route. But interfaces with other pollution control measures are conceptually less clear. They should not be. Unless such uncertainties are clarified, objectives also become unclear, and the possibility exists for large sums of money to be wasted. Where individual measures are used simply to control the input of materials into the environment, irrespective of standards in space and time, then their effectiveness and value needs to be assessed relative to the total quantities entering the environment from all controllable, and even uncontrollable, sources. Equally, efforts to achieve compliance with environmental quality standards at specific points in space and time need to include measures to control both discrete and diffuse sources. This is not easily done; it is not even always considered. But again a failure or inability to consider such aspects will not only prevent the objectives from being achieved, it can also result in the wastage of large sums of money.

15. It may have to be accepted that some putative targeted standards may not be deliverable by pollution control alone. One cannot 'guarantee' exact future biological environmental states. Diffuse sources are not readily amenable to control. This may be overcome to some extent, however, by trimming both the water quality objectives and the relevant pollution control measures to the right scale. This has not yet been achieved, even in relation to international standards being applied nationally – the basis of 'subsidiarity'. More thought needs to be given to interfacing objectives and pollution control measures not only through the derivation of vulnerable, sensitive, and other 'zones' to protect surface and underground sources, but within more sophisticated catchment boundaries.

16. Value for money will only be achieved in such pollution control measures anyway if they are eventually devised on the same basis of risk. Each control is applied because a risk exists; a risk of breaching the objective for short or long periods of time. Cost-risk techniques can then be applied to the most appropriate geographical scale.

WHO BENEFITS, WHO PAYS
17. We still lack even basic tools to combine environmental and economic modelling. There are therefore few, if any, satisfactory analyses available of who, in economic terms, actually benefits from specific water qualities and uses, and who pays to maintain or achieve them. For water, it could be said that everyone benefits and everyone pays - more or less. But the details of the 'more or less', and the perceptions of it, drive the expenditure of large amounts of money. It is clearly necessary to consider both benefits and costs when assessing water quality needs. But it may be difficult, impossible, or even undesirable to attempt to do this in a strictly cost-benefit sense. Its application to the environment can literally lead to estimates of the cost of everything but the value of nothing. The value of the environment, and the benefits of its different qualities, has essentially to be decided by its custodians - the Government - at any

particular time. Achieving or maintaining the quality
objectives of the water resource should therefore not be so
much a matter of cost-benefit, but one of achieving the
objective in the most cost-effective manner. And it is
here, again, that pollution control and environmental
quality standard approaches need to be correctly interfaced
if cost-effective solutions are to be forthcoming.

18. This still leaves open the questions of who should
pay, and who will end up paying. Where poor water results
from current inputs, then it would seem reasonable that the
cost might fall on the discharger. Where such inputs arise
from discharges surviving from past practices, however, the
question is more difficult; but it still has to be answered.
Again a proper scale is required. If the effects of past
practices have a significant detrimental effect, which
frustrates the proper use of water resource management on a
reasonable scale, then a combined effort may be needed to
address the problem for the 'national' good, using the
'national' purse - at least in part. The inability to
provide ready answers to such common problems, however,
arises in part from a failure in the past to manage all of
the sectors of the environment - air, land and water - in an
integrated way. It is about time that significant steps
were taken to address this deficiency. A broader, more
coherent, 'framework' is required.

Wastewater treatment — the costs of meeting quality obligations

A. BOOKER, Deputy Director General, Office of Water Services

SYNOPSIS This paper discusses the review of the water industry price limits which will be completed in July next year. In particular the paper outlines the work which has gone into establishing the new water and environmental quality obligations which will be taken into account in setting new price limits. There is a major issue of affordability for water customers in meeting new and proposed standards. The paper explains the questions posed for Ministers in the Ofwat paper on 'Paying for Quality' and the response of the Secretary of State in the 'Quality Framework'. There are inherent risks for the UK in seeking to role back EC directives which are already in place and in holding up the development of new standards. The risks and priorities should be balanced against questions of affordability and the risks for customers and public to ensure that environmental obligations are implemented at a rate that customers can afford.

SUMMARY

1. Over the last five years water service prices have been increased by 25% over inflation. These price increases have created major problems for some customers. Affordability of water charges has become an issue in many parts of the country. Concern about customer debt and the number of disconnections has added to the disquiet. Customers who have had problems in affording the increases have shown an increasing resistance to water bills. Customers perceive high profits and dividends for water companies being generated at their expense. Water price limits are to be redetermined in July 1994. The Director General of Water Services (DG) has concluded that the price escalator must and can be stopped. In a monopoly business like water, which raises much of its income on what is seen as a taxation base, customer bills need to be affordable. The major factor influencing increases is the drive for higher environmental and water quality standards. These standards are largely imposed by the EC. A major joint initiative by the regulators and the water companies has brought some hope for water customers that quality improvements can be achieved at an affordable rate.

BACKGROUND

2. Water prices are capped by a factor known as the K factor. In 1989-90 when the K factors were set by the Secretary of State for the Environment and Wales the average across the country was about 5% each year from 1990 through to 1995. The DG has now decided that K factors might be regarded has having two components, X and Q. $K = -X + Q$. Water companies ought to deliver existing standards of service and quality for lower prices which would be reflected in the - X factor, rather like other utility price limits. Quality improvements are the feature which distinguish water from the other utilities. The Q factor represents the increases required in water bills to achieve the new obligations of the companies set by the EC and by the UK water quality regulators. Over the last year Ofwat has been engaged in a campaign to moderate the impact of quality improvements to achieve an average K factor across the country of less than 2% compared with the original 5%.

THE COST OF QUALITY

3. In the autumn of 1992 the DG issued a consultation document which set out his assessment of the impact on water bills of existing and new quality obligations.

4. This consultation set out a number of scenario forecasts for customers. It set the scene for an important piece of work which was carried out under the aegis of the Department of the Environment. The key points were that:

- average household water bills will increase from £120 in 1989 to £185 in 1994-95
- by maintaining the current rate of quality improvement they may rise to £215 in 1999 - 2000 and £245 in 2004-05
- to meet new quality standards already agreed since 1989 they may rise to £230 in 1999-2000 and £290 in 2004-05
- to meet possible new standards they may rise to £255 and £345 respectively (in Nov 1992 prices).

PAYING FOR QUALITY

5. The Department of the Environment set up a working group, chaired by a senior member of the Department, and involving Ofwat, Drinking Water Inspectorate, NRA and the water companies. The group developed guidelines for the costing in detail, company-by-company of the quality obligations. It was a major piece of work carried out over a period of six or seven months, which culminated in an Ofwat report to the Secretary of State, which aggregated the costs for the industry as a whole and converted those costs into water bills. The report published in July of this year, set out the aggregate impact of these new obligations based on these detailed company-by-company costs. The key findings were that:

- existing quality obligations could add £36 to the average household rates bill by 1999-2000 and a further £46 by 2004-05
- possible additions would add £54 by 1999-2000, and a further £77 by 2004-05
- by 1999-2000 customers on average income could be paying water bills amounting to 2.3% of their income
- by 1999-2000 a single pensioner on income support could be paying a water bill of over 10% of their income
- Affordability would become a major problem for customers and companies.

6. The Secretaries of State worked through the summer on a response to Paying for Quality. This response was made in October.

THE QUALITY FRAMEWORK
7. The response of the Secretaries of State was encouraging. It set out a series of actions which the Department of the Environment could take, including a re-examination of the implementation of the Urban Waste Water Treatment Directive. It also said that Government would be prepared to re-open discussions with the EC on the timetable for implementing the UWWTD. The main actions proposed were that:

- quality improvements should be affordable
- the water companies need to continue to make efficiency savings to reduce costs
- costs should be taken into account in deciding how and when to place further obligations on water companies
- the Government will ask EC partners to re-examine priorities to focus on the most immediate environmental concerns
- opportunities for cost reducing technical innovation must not be overlooked
- measures which have a reasonable chance of meeting requirements should be adopted rather than those which achieve absolute certainty.

8. Work is now going on to revise the guidelines in the light of the Quality Framework. Companies will undertake their costing exercise over the next four months in preparation for submitting their strategic business plans to Ofwat at the end of March next year. The strategic business plans will inform the determination process for prices, in particular the Q element in the K factor. Setting the level of X will be less a cost plus exercise than that which has had to be adopted for quality improvements. The judgment of the DG will figure more prominently in that exercise.

SETTING PRICE LIMITS

9. On 4 November the DG published a document which set out the framework within which he will set price limits in July next year. The key points from that document are:

* The rapid increase in water prices above the rate of inflation can be moderated in the following ways:

    • companies should be able to provide existing standards of service at prices which are below today's level in real terms
    • companies should fund improvements in standards of service through greater efficiency rather than higher prices
    • price increases should be limited to what is necessary to meet new quality and environmental obligations. The Government has stated that further improvements should be affordable.

* Returns on capital will be lower:

    • for the purpose of setting price limits, the Director will assume a lower return on new investment than that assumed in 1989, reflecting the lower risk that companies now face
    • the higher return allowed at flotation by the Secretaries of State will not be clawed back retrospectively. To respect companies' expectations, the Director would assume that the return on existing capital should converge on the lower return assumed on expenditure over a period of time. The rate would depend on the circumstances of individual companies

* Companies will have scope to increase efficiency and share rewards with shareholders.

* Where companies are investing to meet additional demand:

    • standard infrastructure charges paid for new properties connected to the water supply and sewerage system would be limited to £200 for each service. Phasing in could be considered
    • companies who consider they need significant expansion of their systems, including the provision of new resources, will be required to consider the wider installation of meters.

* The operations of the appointed water and sewerage companies are required to be ring fenced. The Director will not seek to control the diversified business of the group company, but will act to protect the interests of the water customers by preventing cross subsidy.

* There are big differences between the position of individual companies. The paper sets out a qualitative framework for the industry. How it is applied will depend on individual companies' circumstances.

10. The document contains few firm numbers. The detailed numbers, company-by-company need to be worked out over the next nine months. First of all, the companies will develop their estimates in preparation for submitting strategic business plans and then Ofwat will determine the costs which are allowable in the elements which make up K factors. The determinations of the DG could be referred to the MMC if any company is sufficiently aggrieved.

11. The costs of meeting quality obligations will be influenced by an assessment of the various types of risks involved in meeting standards.

RISKS

12. The whole process comprises a number of stages. Standards are set, design and construction is carried out to meet them and facilities are operated to achieve them.

13. The needs of the water industry should be led by customers requirements. These might be based on market research information, from customer complaints, from discussions with Customer Service Committees or customer focus groups. Customers are always likely to want more in the way of results for lower bills. This is in the nature of customer expectation.

14. Efficiency improvements will be needed to enable companies to deliver more improvements than they can afford to provide from conventional techniques. This drive for efficiency creates the incentive for companies to perform better and to examine risks at each stage of the process.

15. Some of the process is not under the control of the companies. They can influence it but they cannot control it directly.

Table 1 - POSSIBLE RISK MATRIX FOR WATER SERVICES

RISKS	FOR WHOM	WHO DECIDES	WHO SHOULD DECIDE
1 Health Standards	Consumers	WHO EC	Customers
2 Aesthetic Standards	Consumers Public	Pressure Groups	Customers
3 Environmental Standards	Public	Pressure Groups	Public/ Customers
4 Service Standards	Customers	Companies	Customers
5 Design Standards	Companies	Companies	Companies
6 Operational	Companies	Companies	Companies
7 Affordability	Customers	Government Ministers	Customers

16. Table 1 shows a possible risk matrix for water services. The matrix indicates who the risk is borne by, who currently decides the level of risk and who ought to decide it. In some areas of risk there is a mis-match between who does, and who should decide the appropriate level. Fortunately this is not the situation with design standards. There is also interaction between the different risks. In competitive markets this interaction operates through conventional market mechanisms. But in regulated markets regulators influence the interaction. This matrix has clear implications for process engineers. Design standards can encompass low or high risk in meeting the standards required.

17. The achievement of process standards could well be a separate sub-matrix. This would address the water companies responsibility for converting standards into results for customers and the division of risk between customers and companies on the basis of cost. The sub-matrix could then look at the design risks involved in meeting the company specification to be achieved and dividing those risks between the company and the contractor, or supplier.

18. In finding a way forward on this difficult issue it is helpful to think in terms of customer supplier chains in identifying risks and costs, and where in the chain the risk might reside. The Secretaries of State are right to highlight the problem and to express their view that some of the business risk should be accepted by the water companies.

24

IMPLICATIONS FOR WATER COMPANIES

19.   Water companies will need to find lower cost solutions to the problems of meeting higher water quality and environmental standards. Traditional processes and construction materials are unlikely to deliver results at an acceptable level of cost. Risks have already been discussed as an element in the cost equation. There are other transaction costs such as type of contract - turn key, BOT etc; plant design - package, modular, bespoke; capacity - over size, or right size and method of procurement - keen competition, negotiated tender. The process engineer working in water and sewage treatment will need to break free of water traditions and employ the techniques used in more commercial situations. The water companies will have incentives to pursue results for customers, not elegant engineering monuments for future generations. They will be looking to process engineers to produce these results. There will be plenty of scope for innovative process research and development. Water and sewage treatment should not for ever be regarded as a single product uniform service. There will be calls for different solutions in different regions, and individuals and groups of customers will look for more individual solutions. There is a challenging time ahead for process engineers and for the water companies to find lower cost solutions. They ought to rise to that opportunity.

CONCLUDING COMMENT

20.   The water industry is moving into a new era. Companies have incentives to achieve higher levels of efficiency in order to sustain profitability. They will need to draw on innovative process research and development to achieve their obligations to meet higher quality standards. They might also decide to examine the risk profile of their business, in particular in meeting higher quality standards. This might lead them to seek to share some of the business risk with their suppliers. The new era will bring downwards pressure on transaction costs which may, in addition, lead to new ways of doing business. Process engineers used to operating in highly competitive process markets will be well placed to take advantage of the situation.

North Tyneside bathing waters scheme

S. J. FRITH, BSc, MICE, MIWEM, Project Manager, and K. D. STAPLES, FICE, FIWEM, Chairman, Montgomery Watson Ltd

SYNOPSIS. The paper describes the development of a scheme to ensure that Bathing Water standards are not prejudiced. The concepts involve an assessment of the frequency of storm sewage discharge from an element of the Tyneside sewerage scheme interceptor overflows serving a population of 75,000 rising to 129,000; the scope for providing storage to reduce the frequency and volume of storm sewage discharge; the engineering of a storm sewage interceptor sewer; and the development of a pumped discharge system through a sea outfall at Brierdene, Whitley Bay.

INTRODUCTION

1.   The North Tyneside Bathing Water Scheme has been designed to ensure compliance with the bathing water quality Directives of the EC when, in times of storm, the existing Tyneside interceptor system is subject to overflow. The North Tyneside area embraces Tynemouth, Cullercoats and Whitley Bay, where sewage is intercepted and conveyed to treatment at Howden on the River Tyne. The recorded exceedence of bathing water quality coliform standards in North Tyneside is related to stormwater discharges when overflow takes place from the interceptor system.

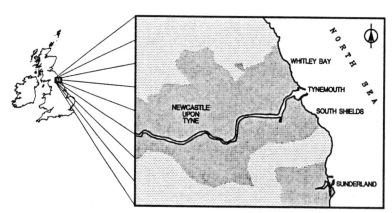

Fig. 1. Location plan

2.   The scheme concepts are derived from a study and evaluation of a number of alternatives but are founded on utilization of storage within the existing interceptor sewer system and provision of a major storm interceptor sewer, both to convey stormwater and provide considerable storage volume with the aim of significantly reducing the frequency of storm sewage discharge to the coast. Provision of a pumping station and screening facility will manage the infrequent discharge of stormwater from the system through a new long sea outfall.

3.   The scheme is one of a number currently being promoted by Northumbrian Water Ltd along its coastline and requires the evaluation, design and construction of large tunnels in coal measures strata and a major storm sewage pumping station in an area of public sensitivity.

4.   The project, estimated to cost some £21M, is required to be complete and commissioned by the end of 1995 to meet a bathing water quality directive deadline.

SCHEME OBJECTIVES

5.   In simple terms, the objective for the Feasibility Studies undertaken by both Entec Europe Ltd (1990) and Montgomery Watson (October 1991) for Northumbrian Water Ltd was the achievement of compliance with the European Directive 76/160/EEC on Bathing Water Quality. Northumbrian Water Ltd were mindful also of further obligations under the European Directive 91/27/EEC on Urban Waste Water.

6.   The Directive schedules Mandatory Standards (I) for bathing waters which must not be exceeded for 95% of the samples taken fortnightly during the bathing season and the guidelines usually associated with an 80% compliance.   The principal directive parameters are:

Table 1 - Bathing Water Quality Directive standards

	Volume	Mandatory	Guideline
Total Coliform	100ml	10,000	500
Faecal Coliform	100ml	2,000	100
Faecal Streptococci	100ml	-	100
Salmonella	1 litre	0	-
Enteroviruses	10 litres	0	-

7.   The Studies debated the contentious interpretation of the requirement within the Bathing Water Directive in Article 5(2) which states that "deviations from the values referred to in Article 3 shall not be taken into consideration in the calculation of the percentage referred to in paragraph 1 when they are the results of floods, other natural disasters or abnormal weather conditions". The meaning of abnormal weather conditions has been the subject of much debate throughout the Community.

8.   Prior to the setting up of the National Rivers Authority, the only published guidance within the United Kingdom to the operation of storm sewage overflows to sea was the HMIP guidance note of November 1988 (guidance on new long sea outfalls - COPA Consent Applications). This indicated, with regard to Article 5/2 of the Bathing Water Directive, that compliance failures due to floods, other natural disasters and abnormal weather conditions may be disregarded.   Note 6 of the guidance note provides an interpretation on the required definition of abnormal weather conditions. It states "Article 5 does allow for the exclusion of failed samples on grounds of abnormal weather conditions. Storms with a predicted return of once in five years or greater are considered of sufficient severity to warrant elimination of unacceptable monitoring results under Article 5; failures attributable to storms of up to one in five years return periods must be consistent with achieving 95% compliance in the receiving waters."

9.   This perceived requirement was fundamental to any option involving the continued use of the existing short sea outfalls and to any proposal to construct new long sea outfalls. The formation of the National Rivers Authority in 1989 provided the statutory body to administrate the legislation. It is now generally accepted that the HMIP guidelines referred to above produce the most widely accepted design criteria for coastal discharges when combined with the requirement for fine screening of all coastal discharges. The recommendation was therefore made to Northumbrian Water Ltd that the options should be considered on this baseline.

10.   In practical terms, the realistic objectives for a project dealing with the disposal of stormwater to a designated Bathing Water can be related to compliance with the mandatory coliform indicator criteria and the avoidance of visible pollution at the shoreline.

HISTORY OF THE SCHEME

11.   Since 1976 sewage flows from the North Tyneside coastal towns of Tynemouth, Cullercoats and Whitley Bay have been passed to the Howdon Sewage Treatment Works on the north bank of the River Tyne for preliminary and primary treatment in combination with all other foul flows from the Tyneside Sewerage System.

12.   Before 1976 foul flows were passed directly to the sea through short sea outfalls along the coastal frontage, all discharging at around mean low water. With the commissioning in 1976 of the North Tyneside, Coastal Interceptor Sewer System, the Tynemouth Interceptor Sewer and the strategic pumping stations at Browns Point, North Point, and Sharpness Point on the coastline, flows of up to about 3.5 DWF were passed forward to treatment. The new interceptor sewers were designed (like all others within the Tyneside Sewerage Scheme) to handle the ultimate 'Tyneside' formula which assumed a large increase in water usage in the area due to the industrial expansion foreseen in the 1950s and 60s and an expected population expansion.

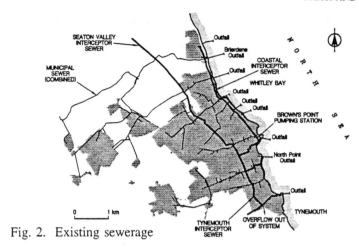

Fig. 2. Existing sewerage

13.   The North Tyneside area has a present population of about 75,000 and a dry weather sewage flow estimated at 160l/s, 13,800m³/d projected to increase to a population of 129,000 and a flow of 445l/s 38,450m³/d.

14.   Excess stormwater overflow from the Coastal Interceptor Sewer system continued to be discharged to the sea through the old combined sewage outfalls, and was suspected to be a major contributory factor in the occasional failure of the beaches to comply with the European Bathing Water Directive. The visual quality of the discharge has been improved in the 1976 works by the installation of screenings plants on all the stormwater overflows discharging to the short sea outfalls, but these provided only coarse screening, usually with 18mm bar spacing, and only two of the outfalls discharge beyond mean low water.

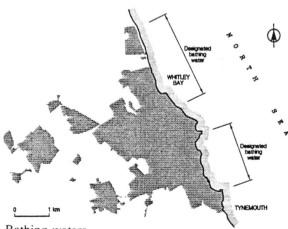

Fig. 3. Bathing waters

Table 2. Summary of bathing water failures

Station	1986	1987	1988	1989	1990	1991
Whitley Sands	-	-	2(2)	2(2)	1(1)	-
Cullercoats	1(0)	1(1)	1(1)	3(1)	-	-
Long Sands North	2(1)	-	-	1(0)	1(1)	-
Long Sands South	-	-	-	-	1(1)	-

Note - Figures in brackets refer to the number of failures which may be attributed to high rainfall. Normal season 1st May - 30th September sampled weekly, normally 20 samples p.a.

15. Aware of the requirement to ensure that all their bathing beaches complied with the European Directive on Bathing Water Quality by 1995, Northumbrian Water Ltd commissioned three consultants to carry out a coastal strategy study for the whole Northumbrian Coastline between Berwick on Tweed and Saltburn.

16. The study objective was to develop a long-term strategy for Northumbrian Water Ltd to enable them to satisfy all their current and foreseeable obligations with respect to coastal discharges.

17. Within the 1989 study the North Tyneside strategy was considered by Entec Europe Ltd, the consultancy company of Northumbrian Water Group. In March 1991 Montgomery Watson was engaged to undertake the feasibility studies for the North Tynside scheme, which encompassed the coastline between the mouth of the River Tyne and St Mary's Island, Whitley Bay.

FEASIBILITY STUDY

18. The Coastal Strategy Study had identified three principle options for the works required in achieving compliance with the bathing water directive. These were:

(a) The extension of all nine existing short sea outfalls to a distance beyond mean low water where they ceased to influence compliance with the bathing water directive.

(b) The storage of all storm flows up to a reasonable level within the existing sewerage system by the addition of storage tanks and its subsequent transfer, within the existing system, to Howdon S.T.W. for treatment.

(c) Construction of two new long sea outfalls at Brown's Point and Brierdene, with associated interceptor sewers providing some storm attenuation, to discharge storm sewage to sea and abandonment of the existing short storm outfalls.

19. Early fieldwork and preliminary cost estimates for extension of all the outfalls to a distance of approximately 1km beyond mean low water demonstrated that the first option was impractical.

20. Retention of all flows arising from all storms up to a 1 in 5 year return frequency is envisaged in the HMIP guidance note and is clearly

desirable on environmental grounds. Use of sewerage simulation models indicated that an additional storage capacity of about 48,000m³ would have to be provided. Multiple storage in the contributory area was ruled out due to lack of available sites in the intensely urbanised areas and the magnitude of the future large-scale maintenance requirements. Vertical storage tanks (shafts) were favoured because of their ability to store large volumes of flows in small footprint locations. There were, however, a number of disadvantages, the principal one being the samll capacity of the receiving sewer and thus the slow emptying of the storage tanks. An occurrence of two substantial storms within a few days of each other would have presented particular difficulty, with the likelihood of tanks still being partially full from the previous event.

21.   Provision of large storage tanks close to the coast was not feasible between Watts Slope and Brown's Point due to a lack of suitable sites. It would consequently be necessary to construct interceptor sewers to carry flows from this area to the northern area where more space was available. The requirement for large-scale storm sewage interceptors added significantly to the estimated costs of this option.

22.   The option of providing one or more new long sea outfalls to pass storm flows to sea presented the most flexible option with regard to future operation. A preliminary cost benefit comparison was undertaken for construction of an additional interceptor sewer to carry stormwater flows to a single location or dividing the area, and constructing two sea outfalls. It was quickly established that storm attenuation in the interceptor would provide storage and time delays which reduced the size of pumping station and outfall required.

23.   To consider the options, a flow simulation model to study the existing system was appropriate and it was decided to construct a macro-sized WALLRUS model of the existing interceptor sewer system and its contributory systems.

24.   Records of the existing sewerage system held by Northumbrian Water Ltd were extensive and in particular, because of its recent construction, the interceptor system was well documented.

25.   The macro-scale WALLRUS model of the system consisted of 300 individual pipes, 7 pumping stations and 18 storm sewage overflows. The model covered a total area of 976 hectares and was broken down so that no single modelled pipe had a contributing area of more than 25 hectares.

26.   The model was created from the existing sewerage records that had been digitized on AUTOCAD and further detailed physical survey work was carried out in the catchment. Due to the timescale of the feasibility study, a detailed verification of the model by flow survey could not be undertaken. To gain confidence in its use as a means for considering different options, a preliminary verification involving 21 key sites was identified, with a flow monitoring survey being undertaken for a month. The results provided sufficient confidence that the model could be used for its intended purpose at that stage. A full verification procedure undertaken during the detailed

design phase confirmed the preliminary results.

27. The assessment addressed the design storm profiles and design storms for 1, 5 and 40 year return periods and durations from 1 to 12 hours were modelled. It was established that storm water volumes of over $140,000m^3$ would reach the coast on a 5 year return period storm over 12 hours, with the facility to pump forward to treatment approximately $90,000m^3$ in the same period.

28. Development of a dynamic model allowed the performance of the projected stormwater interceptor sewer running north from Browns Point to Brierdene to be demonstrated. Essentially, the model output considered a variety of storms, the outflow from the coastal sewage interceptor, the available storage in the stormwater sewer and the consequent rate of outflow to a single sea outfall at Brierdene required to protect the system.

29. The sizing of the proposed interceptor sewer and pumped outfall were based on flows from 5 year storms. In order to determine how frequently the outfall would operate during a typical year, and what volumes of flow it would pass, a set of ranked storm events for a typical year was needed. The North East storm set was found to be suspect, so it was decided to use the Yorkshire set, collected over 30 years at Finningley, near Doncaster. Standard average annual rainfall at the site is comparable with that at Whitley Bay, being around 650mm, and M5-60 is also very similar at 16mm, so the storms can be used without correction.

30. Results from running selected events through the main model showed that some 70 events per year will cause spills to the new interceptor sewer, of which between 5 and 10 will be of sufficient magnitude to require the outfall to operate. It is assumed that spills below about $5000m^3$ can be retained and entirely returned to the existing coastal interceptor sewer once the storm has subsided. The total volume of flows passing through the new outfall will be in the order of $100,000 - 150,000m^3$ in a typical year, representing around 10 hours of outfall operation at a discharge rate of $3.75m^3/s$.

MARINE DISPOSAL EVALUATION

31. Storm flow modelling showed that more than three quarters of the total predicted run off occurred in the area between North Parade and North Point at the southern end of the catchment. The storm attenuation provided by locating a new storm outfall at North Point therefore would be comparatively small. Consideration of a single outfall located towards the northern-most point of the catchment at Brierdene, with an interceptor sewer running north from North Point to Brierdene was clearly indicated as the most cost-effective solution for a sea outfall option. In order to consider the favoured locations from a discharge dispersal point of view, Montgomery Watson commissioned Northumbrian Water's Model Services Group to carry out coastal modelling utilising the NORDOS Coastal model developed by W S Atkins for the Durham Coastal region. This model has a coarse mesh size

of 250m, which made it less than ideal for evaluating short outfalls and stormwater dispersion. To increase confidence in the understanding of water movements, the client's Analytical and Environmental Services Group undertook drogue float tracking from specific locations, varying between 300m and 1300m beyond mean low water, in the vicinity of the favoured outfall sites. This drogue tracking indicated that Brierdene would be strongly favoured in comparison with intervening or adjoining sites as a location for a new outfall when considering dispersion of the discharge.

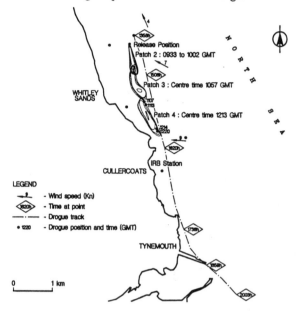

Fig. 4. Marine dispersion

32. Subsequently, at the instigation of the NRA, a dye release and a sampling exercise from the proposed location was organised under adverse weather conditions which demonstrated confidence in the design assessment.

33. A statistical analysis considered tidal movement and wind, which were the principal processes likely to cause storm sewage discharged offshore to move towards the beach. The critical wind direction is onshore, which for North Tyneside would be wind coming from a direction of between 330° and 150°. Records show that on-shore winds could be expected to occur approximately 16% of the time.

34. The main direct onshore movement will be induced by the wind and have its maximum effect (minimum movement time to shoreline) during periods of slack water. The rate of onshore movement was assessed and equated to a maximum of about 1.5% of the wind speed. Taking the combination of a force 5/6 onshore wind from the critical sector and a period of about 1 hour after a discharge at slack water, it is calculated that the onshore drift in the worst case could be 750m.

35.   To finalise the length of the outfall, the critical onshore movement of a distance of 200m was added to 750m to allow protection to bathers from the beach. This produced a proposed distance of 950m beyond the mean low water as an appropriate length of outfall.

INVESTIGATIONS AND STUDIES
Flow Surveys

36.   To validate the flow models for detailed design required a full verification following an extensive flow monitoring survey undertaken by Total Flow Surveys. 37 sites for flow monitors and ten sites for rain gauges throughout and downstream of the catchment were utilised. Work on the survey began in January 1992 but prolonged dry weather delayed the capture of sufficient data for a full standard verification of the model until August 1992.

37.   Verification proceeded immediately the information become available and proceeded well with a good correlation being identified. In a few areas re-survey was necessary and errors in sewerage details were found. To complete the verification process, an audit was carried out by Model Services Group and, for application to the final design, the model was transferred to SPIDA which provided better information on storage.

Ground Investigation

38.   Site investigation, to assess ground conditions both onshore and offshore, was of critical importance to the design of the scheme. Exploration Associates undertook the work and a evaluation was discussed with Montgomery Watson specialist staff. Over eighty boreholes were sunk to investigate the geology of the North Tyneside Coal Measures Strata including fourteen offshore.   From the result, reference ground conditions were produced for the main tunnel and outfall works as a baseline for the proposed contracts.   Of particular importance was the probability of encountering abandoned mine workings on the tunnel route.

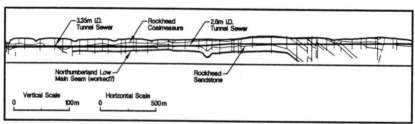

Fig. 5. Geological section (along tunnel centreline)

Siltation Investigation

39.   Modelling work indicated that of the approximate 11,500m³ of storage available in the downstream large diameter storage section of the pipe around 5,000m³ could be deemed operational storage.   To ensure ease of maintenance, consideration was given to the possibility of extensive siltation

taking place in this large sewer, Hydraulics Research Ltd were commissioned to carry out modelling to estimate the amounts of siltation likely to be experienced and assess whether artificial forms of flushing may be necessary to assist in sewer cleansing. Results show that some limited siltation is to be expected but that efficient functioning of the 18mm protection screenings plants on each storm sewage overflow feeding the new interceptor sewer, coupled with natural flushing in storm events, would limit the amount of siltation to manageable proportions. Only very infrequent mechanical cleaning is envisaged and the provision of flushing tanks was not found to be cost-effective. Each tank would have only a localised effect and a large number of tanks and high water usage would be needed.

Consents

40. Parallel to the development of the design, extensive discussions were held with the National Rivers Authority to obtain discharge consent for the proposed new long sea outfall. The Authority accepted the statistical basis of the design of the outfall but, in view of the limited hydrographic modelling and surveys, they required a dye-tracking and dispersion survey to reinforce the previous work.

Environmental Impact and Planning Permissions

41. The project and the engineering proposals were the subject of an Environmental Impact Study carried out by Travers Morgan. This confirmed the basic objectives and provided support to the Planning application for the pumping station.

Public Awareness

42. Northumbrian Water Ltd, who are most concerned to obtain and retain the support of the public in the North Tyneside area, have devoted considerable effort to this issue. Senior staff from the Water Company, assisted by consultants, have sought to fully inform the local Council, North Tyneside MBC and members of the public.

43. Locally leaflets have been distributed, an exhibition established and house-to-house contact made with nearby residents and others most likely to be affected by the scheme and construction process.

44. The success of this public relations work has been demonstrated by the award of Planning permissions without objection and the present lack of serious complaint as construction progresses.

THE PROJECT

Stormwater Interceptor Sewerage

45. The interceptor sewer, which extends for 3.6km between North Point, Tynemouth and Brierdene, Whitley Bay, is to be constructed in tunnel with the initial section between North Point and Watts Slope (Shafts WB1 to WB11) of 2.10m finished internal diameter. Designed purely to act as a carrier sewer, this section of the interceptor is sized to carry peak flows only. Eleven shafts 4.57m in diameter are required at depths varying between 7 and 13m. Six are points of connection for the existing sewerage system. The

tunnels, designed conventionally to have primary segmental linings with in situ concrete secondary linings, are to be driven almost entirely in coal measures rock with a number of fault zones and mineworkings to be crossed.

46.   From Watts Slope northwards, (Shafts WB11 to Brierdene Pumping Station) the tunnel is enlarged to 3.35m finished internal diameter and this 1.3km length provides the attenuation storage for storm flows. Again, the tunnel design was conventional and ground conditions are more problematical, with large numbers of disused mine shafts to be avoided. Five manhole shafts up to 15m deep and 5.29m diameter are included in this section.

47.   In the event, the tunnel sewers are to proceed with the use of three tunnelling machines erecting a single pass segment, a design offered by and agreed with the successful Contractor.

Brierdene Pumping Station

48.   The pumping station is designed to pass the storm sewage through 6mm screens and pump a peak flow of 3.75m^3/sec.

49.   The site for the pumping station, in a tourist area, is very sensitive and the planning authority was anxious to avoid a superstructure extending above the surrounding ground level where it would affect the views from adjacent housing. The use of the dene to site the station allowed a comparatively small footprint design but the problems of accommodating the screening plant were a major obstacle to this objective. Use of drum screens was considered but the area required was too large and therefore band screens were adopted. The use of band screens on storm sewage is innovative, with only a limited number of plants operating in the United

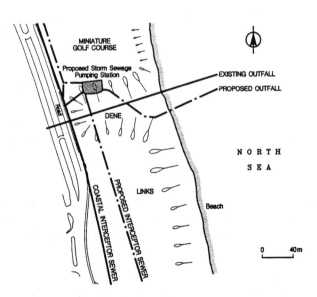

Fig. 6. Pumping station and outfall site plan

Kingdom. Three 13m long screen units are to be provided, two duty and one standby, liberally rated to cater for the maximum throughflow. Two duty and one standby Centrifugal Storm Sewage Pumps capable of pumping $2m^3/s$ each are to be provided.

50.   In addition, to cater for the large number of small storms which will feed the interceptor sewer, a secondary well is provided to return storm flow to the existing sewerage system at a maximum rate of 250l/s.   These submersible pumps also return screenings flushed from the screenings plant.

51.   Significant environmental improvements planned and designed around the station included new footbridges and public toilets.   Hard and soft landscaping will ensure that the pumping station blends into the dene and retains its seaside character.   Deodorization to the pumping station is provided by a forced air ventilation system and wet scrubber deodorization plant.

Sea Outfall

52.   Brierdene Sea Outfall has already been constructed and is 1050m long, 1200mm diameter and sited in rock beneath the sea bed.   Steel pipes with an external high density concrete weightcoat 112mm thick are protected against external corrosion protection by coal tar enamel reinforced with a glass tissue wrap.   Internal protection is a 1.5mm thick coating of 'Durethane P', a 100% solids urethane pitch lining, factory-applied over the majority of the pipe length and hand-applied for the site tie in string joints.

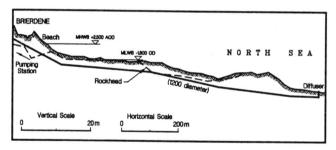

Fig. 7. Outfall section

53.   The outfall has a four port diffuser which will be fitted with 700mm diameter 'Tideflex' non-return valves on commissioning to prevent seawater ingress in the intervals between the infrequent operation of the outfall.   The discharge assembly is protected from damage by a precast concrete dome structure.

54.   Trench excavation up to 7m deep was required beneath the sea bed, with offshore excavation involving blasting within sections of the coal measure strata.   The design was based on the bottom pull method of installation.

PROJECT MANAGEMENT

55.   The scheme is one in Northumbrian Water Ltd's current major capital works programme and the public perception of such a scheme in a sensitive

tourist area is most important to the Company.

56. Management of the project programme includes very rigorous cost control which necessitates detailed attention to all these matters.

57. The Client, recognising these objectives, has organised a partnership between all relevant parties to the scheme, with their own Project Manager based on site and assisted by Turner and Townsend Project Management as Project Co-ordinators. Public Relations and Financial Management are handled by this locally-based team and provisions have been included in certain key contracts for promotional activities commensurate with the nature of the work.

58. The Engineer remains responsible for the design and contract administration, assisted by site supervisory staff led by the Chief Resident Engineer.

ESTIMATED COSTS AND PROJECT MANAGEMENT

59. The project studies, design and award of contracts has been accomplished within a very short programme. The need to reach a decision and progress to obtain completion and achievement of the consent compliance has driven the project. The adopted and partially-achieved programme is shown in Figure 8 and the projected contract division and estimated costs in Table 3.

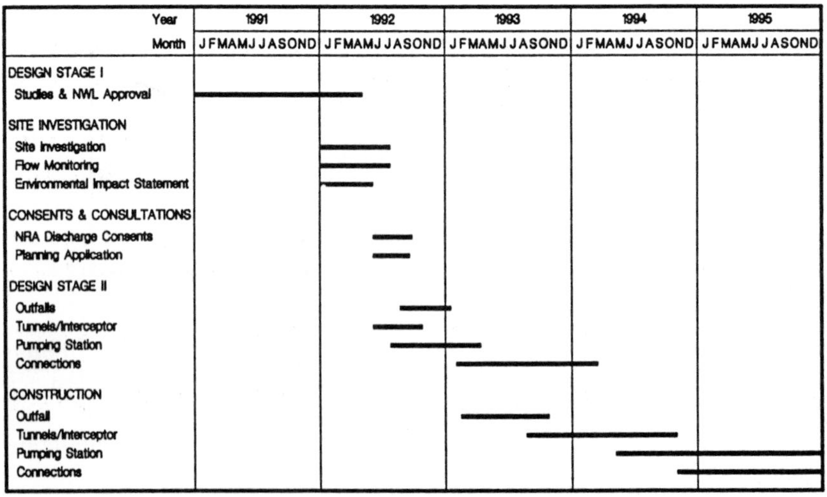

Year	1991	1992	1993	1994	1995
Month	JFMAMJJASOND	JFMAMJJASOND	JFMAMJJASOND	JFMAMJJASOND	JFMAMJJASOND
DESIGN STAGE I					
Studies & NWL Approval					
SITE INVESTIGATION					
Site Investigation					
Flow Monitoring					
Environmental Impact Statement					
CONSENTS & CONSULTATIONS					
NRA Discharge Consents					
Planning Application					
DESIGN STAGE II					
Outfalls					
Tunnels/Interceptor					
Pumping Station					
Connections					
CONSTRUCTION					
Outfall					
Tunnels/Interceptor					
Pumping Station					
Connections					

Fig. 8. Project programme

Table 3 - Estimated project costs

Contract/Works	Contractor	Estimated Costs (£000)
PRELIMINARY		
Studies and Designs including Site Investigation	Various	1400
Site Supervision	Various	900
CONSTRUCTION		
Interceptor Sewer	Kennedy Construction	8000
Outfall	Van Oord ACZ	2500
Pumping Station Civil	-	2500
Pumps	Weir	430
Screens	Three Star	400
Ancillary Works	-	750
Connections	-	2100
Power Supplies	-	210
Land and Utilities and General	-	900
TOTAL	-	21,000

CONCLUSIONS

60.   The project has presented an interesting challenge to the design team, who have to meet the construction completion deadline in 1995 from the commencement of the feasibility study in 1992.

61.   The combination of storm sewage interception and transfer, with storage to attenuate the flows and greatly reduce the volume and frequency of discharge to sea, is relatively novel.

62.   The assessment and design optimisation has only been possible by the iterative use of flow simulation models against a range of conceptual engineering options.

63.   The consequent combination solution of flow transfer, storage, screening and discharge to sea with dilution offshore has provided a modern optimised solution to the project objective, which is to protect the adjoining bathing waters.

ACKNOWLEDGEMENTS

64.   The authors wish to thank the Engineering Director of Northumbrian Water Ltd for permission to publish this paper and the many colleagues and friends in Montgomery Watson Ltd who encouraged the authors and assisted in the development of the paper.

Quality improvements and objectives in the Trent catchment

J. R. MARTIN, Effluent Quality Planner, Severn Trent Water Ltd, and
D. J. BREWIN, Regional Water Quality Manager, National Rivers
Authority, Severn Trent Region

SYNOPSIS. The River Trent and several of its main tributaries
were formerly grossly polluted. Over the last 30 years major
improvements have been made. Initially these resulted from the
introduction of consent control on discharges. More recently
investment in sewerage and sewage treatment has been directed
at achieving compliance with consent conditions and meeting
specified river quality objectives. The Trent is increasingly
being considered as a source of water resources.

INTRODUCTION
1. The River Trent and several of its major tributaries have
historically been severely polluted by discharges of
inadequately treated sewage and industrial effluents and by
overflows from unsatisfactory sewerage systems. The
implementation of the Rivers (Prevention of Pollution) Acts of
1951 and 1961 stimulated a period of considerable investment and
improvement. More recently a further period of increased
investment has resulted from the implementation in 1985 of Part
II of the 1974 Control of Pollution Act (COPA II) and
subsequently from the processes of water industry privatisation
and establishment of the National Rivers Authority under the
1989 Water Act.
2. This paper gives a brief account of earlier quality
improvements in the catchment but focuses on the achievements
of more recent sewerage and sewage treatment works investment
programmes and on the benefits of other approaches to water
quality improvement, in particular the River Tame purification
lakes. The current quality position is compared with existing
and likely future quality objectives. The implications of
changes in the patterns of industrial activity and increased use
of the Trent, directly or indirectly, for water resources are
outlined. The prospects for future improvements are assessed.

DESCRIPTION OF THE TRENT CATCHMENT
3. The Trent rises in the moorlands of Staffordshire and flows
for 274 km to Trent Falls at which point it joins the Humber
Estuary which then discharges to the North Sea. The Trent
catchment (Fig. 1) covers an area of 10,450 sq km and has a
total population of about 6 million.

Fig.1 The Trent Catchment

4.   About 11 km from its source the Trent flows through the
conurbation of Stoke-on-Trent and the other towns of the
Potteries. The presence of such a large industrial area so near
to its source where dilution is very limited has been a major
cause of pollution.   The Trent and its tributary the Fowlea
Brook have been grossly polluted by unsatisfactory combined
sewer   overflows,   sewage   treatment   works   and   industrial
discharges.   In addition to its potteries, a variety of other
industry including mining and iron and steel processing has been
carried on in this area.
5.   Similar problems on an even larger scale have occurred in
the densely populated areas of the Black Country and Birmingham
which also grew rapidly during the last century as a result
primarily of their extensive metal finishing industries.   The
headwaters of the Tame are located within the urban areas so
problems resulting from low dilution for storm overflows, urban
run-off and effluents are considerable.   Minworth sewage
treatment works which is situated downstream of the conurbation
treats a dry weather flow of about 400 Ml/d and receives less
than 1:1 dilution in the Tame.   At its confluence with the
Trent, the dry weather flow of the Tame is about twice that of

41

the Trent and about 75 percent of its flow is made up of treated sewage effluents.

6.   Downstream of Burton, the flow of the Dove enters the Trent. Water from the Dove is abstracted just upstream of its confluence with the Trent and pumped to reservoirs at Staunton Harold and Foremark which supply Leicester. Although the Dove itself has always been relatively clean, the River Churnet, a tributary of the Dove which includes the town of Leek in its catchment, has suffered pollution from discharges from metal processing industries and textile wastes as well as from sewage effluents. Colour has been a particular problem.

7.   The Derwent catchment is also of major importance as a water resource with impounding reservoirs in its headwaters and the recently constructed regulating reservoir at Carsington securing increased yields for abstractions supplying the East Midlands. Several of the smaller tributaries such as the River Amber receive significant discharges from mining activity and local textile industries as well as sewage effluents.

8.   Before reaching Nottingham, flows from the Rivers Soar and Erewash enter the Trent. The Soar drains a largely agricultural catchment but also receives significant discharges from the Leicester and Loughborough sewage treatment works. The Erewash catchment which drains part of the East Midlands coalfield also receives discharges of treated sewage effluent from a number of industrial towns.

9.   Downstream of Nottingham, the Trent receives the discharge from Stoke Bardolph sewage works, the second largest in the catchment. Although the Trent has covered only about half its total length at this point, it has received over 90 percent of its total sewage and industrial effluent load.

10.   The most significant tributary downstream of Nottingham is the River Idle draining what has until recently been an important mining area though this activity is being drastically reduced.

11.   Nearly 30 percent of the national generating capacity of the UK is located in the Trent catchment and the Trent is a major source of cooling water, though patterns of use are changing.

12.   The nature of the historical industrial activity in areas of the catchment such as the Black Country and Potteries has left a legacy of contaminated land which is a significant source of pollutants. Finally, it is important to recognise that despite the high level of urbanisation and industrialisation, the catchment contains many rural areas and agriculture is also an important activity.

POLLUTION PROBLEMS AND IMPROVEMENTS PRIOR TO 1979

13.   The rapid expansion of industry and associated growth of towns during the last century led to extensive use of rivers to dispose of untreated or inadequately treated sewage, industrial effluents and overflows from combined sewers which were often overloaded. Despite attempts to develop solutions to these problems, lack of an appropriate control framework · and disruption of investment during the two world wars led to a

continuing decline in river quality.

14. The Trent catchment was probably at its worst during the late 1950s. At this time considerable stretches of river were grossly polluted. The Trent River Board (TRB) reported that in the Stoke-on-Trent area reaches of the Trent and Fowlea Brook were considered to be a potential danger to public health. The whole 80 km of the River Tame and some reaches of the Erewash were similarly classified. During the summer months, anaerobic conditions were experienced in the Tame and in the Trent between the Tame and Dove confluences. The quality of the Trent at Nottingham was broadly similar to that of a treated sewage effluent (Fig. 2).

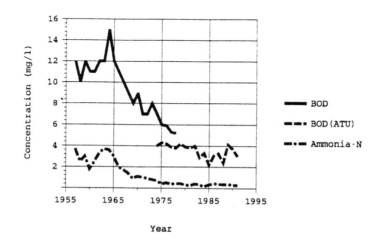

. Fig. 2 Quality of River Trent at Trent Bridge Nottingham

15. Establishment of the Trent River Board and the introduction of consent control for discharges under the Rivers (Prevention of Pollution) Acts of 1951 and 1961 ushered in a period of considerable investment in sewerage and sewage treatment improvements. The provisions of the 1937 Public Health (Drainage of Trade Premises) Act also began to be actively implemented in Birmingham after 1956 (ref. 1). The TRB in reporting on river quality for the period 1957 to 1961 noted the appearance of sewage fungus in parts of the Tame previously unable to support even such a lowly form of life and commented that this might be regarded as a step forward. The Board attributed this improvement to large scale diversion of trade effluents to sewer (ref 2).

16. Prior to 1974, responsibility for sewage treatment rested largely with local authorities. In areas such as the Black Country this had resulted in the presence of many works in close proximity. Where responsibility was vested in a body with

43

responsibility for a wider area, as in Birmingham, the development of larger centralised works frequently formed the basis of the sewerage and sewage treatment improvement strategy. Thus treatment for the Birmingham area was centralised at Minworth which was greatly improved and extended during the 1960s. Similarly, treatment for the Stoke-on-Trent area has become focused at Strongford on the Trent downstream of the conurbation.

17. The overall impact of developments during this period can again be seen in terms of the improving quality at Nottingham (Fig. 2).

18. An extensive study known as the Trent Research programme which examined future water resource needs in the catchment was undertaken during 1968 to 1971 (ref 3). Various strategies for meeting such needs and the potential benefits to water resources of cleaner rivers were examined using mathematical models. Studies on the effects of purification lakes on the River Tame were amongst the possibilities investigated.

19. When Severn Trent Water Authority (STWA) assumed overall responsibility for water supply, sewage treatment and pollution control in the catchment in 1974, the general trend towards centralised treatment facilities continued. In the Tame catchment a scheme was developed for closing most of the 12 sewage treatment works in the Black Country and sewering their flows via a trunk sewer to Minworth thereby utilising existing capacity created by changing patterns of industrial activity and a lower rate of growth than had been anticipated (ref. 4). There are currently only 4 works remaining in the upper Tame catchment though at least one further closure remains a possibility.

QUALITY OBJECTIVES

20. Before 1979 no formal river quality objectives (RQOs) were in place. Consents set by the Trent River Board and Trent River Authority were generally set at the Royal Commission level of 30 mg/l suspended solids, 20 mg/l BOD. It was recognised that selective tightening of such consents might be necessary in due course where dilution was low.

21. In line with the National Water Council proposals for a system of effluent consents and river quality objectives based on 95th percentile quality (ref. 5), the rivers in the catchment were classified according to their existing quality and uses and also, following extensive consultation, given longer term quality objectives. The classification scheme is summarised in Table 1). It was was intended to be broadly compatible with the four class system previously used by DoE for national river quality surveys carried out in 1958 and 1970.

22. The RQOs were set in accordance with the following principles:

- no deterioration from existing river quality;
- class 4 rivers to be eliminated;
- class 3 rivers to be upgraded unless impracticable;
- class 1 and 2 rivers normally to remain in existing class.

Table 1 River Classification Scheme

Class	Intended Uses	D.O. (% sat)	BOD(ATU)	Ammonia-N
1A	Water supply Game fishery	>80	3	0.3
1B	As 1A	>60	5	0.7
2	Water supply[1] Coarse fishery	>40	9	-[2]
3	Industrial	>10	17	-
4		<10	-	-

NB. Limits for BOD and ammonia are 95 percentile upper limits as mg/l, 5 percentiles for DO % saturation.

[1] Class 2 suitable for water supply after advanced treatment.
[2] Class 2 ammonia controlled by requirement to be non-toxic to fish.

23.   Following their publication, it was intended that achievement of the RQOs would become a major factor in determining the need for investment and setting discharge consents. As discussed below, this process has been slower than anticipated owing to limitations on resources available for water quality improvements and the need to carry out major investment programmes simply to achieve compliance with existing sewage treatment works consents and maintain river quality.
24. Fig. 3 demonstrates the changing class of the major rivers of the Trent catchment in terms of classes 1 to 4. This shows the considerable improvements achieved in the 1960s and early 1970s. It also shows some deterioration in 1990 due to earlier under-investment. This trend has since been reversed due to investment from the late 1980s onwards, the benefit of which was not fully reflected in the 1990 survey.
25. The rivers of the Trent catchment are also subject to EC environmental standards such as those for Surface Water for Abstraction (75/440/EEC), Dangerous Substances (76/464/EEC) and its various daughter directives and Freshwater Fisheries (78/659/EEC). (Ref. 6 lists relevant EC Directives).
26. In 1979 1,008 km of the rivers in the catchment were designated under the Freshwater Fisheries Directive as salmonid (263 km) or cyprinid (745 km). NRA now reports annually on compliance to DoE. The 1993 return (1992 data) showed 6 stretches had failed to comply and in such cases NRA has to prepare an action plan with timescales for meeting the failed standard. Failure of the Trent downstream of Nottingham has led NRA to a implement phased requirements for nitrification at Stoke Bardolph sewage works.

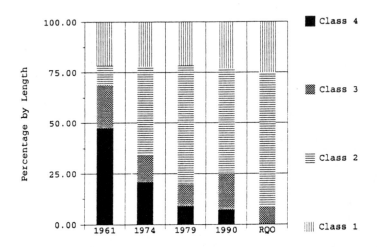

Fig. 3 Trends in Classification of the Major Rivers

27. More recent directives which will affect water quality are the Urban Wastewater Treatment Directive (91/271/EEC) and the Nitrate Directive (91/676/EEC). These require the identification of areas sensitive or vulnerable because of high phosphate or nitrate concentrations. The likelihood of designations within the catchment is discussed below (paras. 42 and 46).
28. The Water Act 1989 made provision for the introduction of statutory water quality objectives (WQOs). These will be set by the Secretary of State, advised by NRA, and will in due course replace the existing RQO system and formally implement the necessary EC limits where appropriate (refs. 6-7).

SEWERAGE AND SEWAGE TREATMENT IMPROVEMENT PROGRAMMES
29. In the early 1980s, most sewage works consents were reviewed to 95 percentile concentration limits based on the capability of existing treatment plant. Prior to the implementation of COPA II in 1985, uncertainty as to how compliance with such consents should be assessed was resolved by the introduction by DoE of the "look-up-table" to control the risk of works being classified as failures purely due to statistical sampling error.
Despite these measures, limitations on investment in a period of severe restraint on public expenditure resulted in an

unacceptably high level of works failure in the mid-1980s.
30. In 1987 following an extensive review of the need for an
asset renewal programme to improve and maintain compliance and
also of the consents required to achieve the RQOs, Severn Trent
Water Authority produced a sewage treatment strategy aimed at
achieving full compliance with existing consents by 1990 and
also achieving RQO related consents at certain specified works.
31. This strategy, known as the COPA II programme, was
incorporated into Severn Trent Water's investment programme
following privatisation of the water industry in England and
Wales under the 1989 Water Act (now generally referred to as
AMP1 where AMP stands for Asset Management Plan). The overall
investment programme included improvements at a number of works
issued with time-limited consents in 1989 and also a large
amount of asset renewal work . At the time of privatisation in
1989 the anticipated expenditure on sewage treatment in the
Severn Trent region over the next ten years was about £1 billion
(ref. 8). Of this the COPA II programme constituted almost 50
percent.
32. This capital programme, in conjunction with initiatives to
improve treatment plant operation has involved work at many
sites and yielded very significant improvements in compliance
(Fig. 4) which for sanitary determinands is at an exceedingly
high level (approximately 99 percent of works comply).

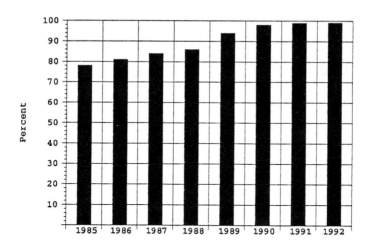

Fig. 4 Percentage of Works Complying with Sanitary Consents

33. Particularly large schemes have included the rebuilding
of Cannock works as an activated sludge plant, construction of
a parallel works extension at Leicester sewage works (Wanlip)
and extensive rebuilding and extension of the Leek works to
enable colour removal to be carried out. Asset renewal at many
small works has involved the installation of Rotating Biological

Contactor (RBC) units with reed bed tertiary or storm treatment if required.

34. In addition to the improved compliance illustrated in Fig. 4, this investment has reflected in improved river quality since the 1990 survey.

35. As well as improving sewage works over this period, considerable investment has been made in sewerage improvements. Knowledge and understanding of the sewerage systems in the catchment has been advanced by carrying out a programme of drainage area studies backed by hydraulic modelling. This programme is now almost complete. Over the last few years, sewerage expenditure for the Severn Trent region has been running at about £80 million per annum.

RIVER TAME PURIFICATION LAKES

36. The idea of constructing purification lakes on the River Tame was first conceived in the mid 1960s and their feasibility was investigated during the Trent Research Programme using a small pilot plant and then two experimental lakes. The quality of the River Tame deteriorated appreciably at times of heavy rainfall due to the premature discharge of combined sewer overflows and the poor quality of run-off from the upstream urban area in Birmingham and the Black Country. The suspended solids load carried by the river increased 100 fold at times of storms and because of the nature of the solids there was a corresponding increase in oxygen demand in the downstream rivers. At times this resulted in the lower Tame and Trent becoming deoxygenated.

37. The first purification lake on the Tame was completed at Lea Marston in 1982. Its total area is 25 hectares and average depth 2.5 metres. Under average flow conditions, the retention time is 12 hours. This allows suspended solids to settle out and these are removed by a dredger for disposal off-site. In 1986 a further lake of area 18 hectares was completed. In 1989 the ownership and operation of the lakes was vested in the Severn Trent region of the NRA.

38. Major improvements in the sewerage systems since the lakes were originally planned, including the use of settlement facilities on surface water sewers, have greatly reduced the pollution load in the river under storm conditions. However, the lakes are still effective at reducing BOD and solids concentrations as shown in Table 2. There is on average a 20 percent removal of BOD through the lakes and at storm times up to 90 percent of the solids are retained in the lake system. Ammonia concentrations increase through the system, however, probably owing to the breakdown of organic nitrogen in the benthic sludge layer. An investigation into the cause of this increase and into the operation of the lakes is being undertaken by NRA with the aim of reducing or eliminating this increase.

39. As well as removing BOD and solids, heavy metal concentrations are reduced by the lakes. Seepage from contaminated land sites in the upper catchment accounts for 30 percent of the heavy metal concentrations in the Tame. The lakes provide the only form of treatment for many of these

discharges.

Table 2. Lea Marston Lakes: Average Quality 1992

Location	BOD	Solids	NH_4-N	DO	Copper	Zinc
Lea Marston (U/S Lakes)	7.6	19	1.4	6.5	42	150
Coton Lane (D/S Lake 1)	6.9	15	2.1	6.1	36	143
Kingsbury (D/S Lakes)	5.9	14	1.9	6.4	35	138

Data are as mg/l except for copper and zinc which are ug/l

WATER RESOURCES DEVELOPMENTS
40.   The Trent has been considered as a potential source of potable water on a number of occasions in the past but it was not until 1990 that a licence was issued for it to be used as drinking water.   This was not for a direct abstraction but for a pumped transfer to the Fossdyke Canal at Torksey and thus via the Rivers Witham and Ancholme to the Elsham treatment works serving South Humberside.   Previously the licence had been for an industrial supply only.   With the demand for new drinking water sources in East Anglia and the South East of England, the River Trent is now being considered as a major future resource for these areas.   South Staffordshire Waterworks Company and Severn Trent Water also have proposals to take future supplies from the Trent.

Table 3.   River Trent: 95th Percentile Quality (mg/l) 1992

Location	NH_4	NO_3	SO_4	Cl	K	Na
Yoxall	0.71	12.1	238	199	19.5	150
Nottingham	0.63	11.8	196	159	13.2	143
Torksey	0.99	12.3	230	161	12.8	138
EC Standard	1.50	11.3	250	200[*]	12.0[*]	150

[*]   Values from water supply regulations.
      Chloride is a guide limit

41.   Table 3 gives a summary of quality data in the river reaches where future abstractions are being considered.   The determinands listed are those where there are potential failures of the standards in the Surface Water Abstraction or Drinking Water Directives.   In the past, much of the focus on cleaning

up water quality in the Trent catchment has been on the criteria used in the NWC classification scheme such as BOD, ammonia and dissolved oxygen. However, as Table 3 shows, increasing use of the Trent as a source of potable water will require the control of other determinands such as nitrate, sulphate, chloride and potassium. Concentrations of these substances are already near to or exceeding the Directive's standards. As use of the Trent increases there will be a greater need to control them at source.

42. With no direct abstractions from the Trent, there is no widespead need at the present time to remove nutrients in order to meet the requirements of the Nitrate Directive or Urban Wastewater Treatment Directives. This may change as more use is made of the river.

43. Increasing chloride concentrations are also a potential problem. Chloride concentrations are already high along the Trent and will be influenced by future plans for certain types of discharge to the catchment. Minewater contributes a major chloride load to the Trent but future levels will depend on the colliery closure programme, and the fate of the minewater once a colliery is closed. Another potential source of chloride is the effluent from nitrate removal plants at water treatment works where ion exchange is used. Such discharges have been discouraged even where they could go to sewer.

44. A further source of chloride is the introduction of flue gas desulphurisation plants (FGD) at power stations. The FGD effluent treatment plant at Ratcliffe-on-Soar will be authorised to discharge 160 tonnes per day of chloride at a point upstream of the Torksey abstraction and other potential abstraction points. To limit the impact the effluent has at low flows, the authorisation requires that the load discharged be reduced as upstream river flows drop below specified values. Nitrate loadings from the treatment plant are similarly controlled to lessen their impact as river flows recede. The authorisation also includes limits for toxic substances including cadmium, mercury and arsenic set at levels to ensure compliance with downstream environmental quality standards.

OTHER CURRENT ISSUES
EC Urban Wastewater Treatment Directive
45. Meeting the basic requirement of this Directive for secondary treatment at works serving equivalent populations in excess of 2000 will not bring significant environmental improvements to the Trent catchment. Most large works which have a significant impact on river quality already produce effluent qualities comparable to or better those required by the Directive. It is anticipated that special measures may be needed at some works to comply with the COD limits in the Directive but their extent depends on the detailed implementation of the Directive. This is still under discussion at the time of writing (December 1993). The sewerage provisions of the Directive are broadly in line with existing policies but may result in the priorities for some schemes being adjusted.
46. As outlined above, extensive designation of sensitive areas

with consequent requirements for nutrient removal is not anticipated. Two areas appear likely to be designated: Kings Mill Reservoir and the River Blythe. The former is a small reservoir used for sailing and other recreational activities on the headwaters of the Maun between Sutton in Ashfield and Mansfield. It receives sewage effluent from Sutton in Ashfield works and has a history of problems due to excessive algal growth. The Blythe is a tributary of the River Tame which drains a catchment to the East of Birmingham which until recently was predominantly rural but the character of which has changed significantly due to development in the Solihull area. The Blythe is abstracted for public supply close to its confluence with the Tame and is also designated a Site of Special Scientific Interest.

Future RQO Achievement

47. A further issue is the rate at which progress might be made in future towards achieving the RQOs or in due course Statutory WQOs. In so far as this involves water company expenditure on sewerage and sewage treatment, the Secretary of State for Environment and Director General of Water Services have recently expressed their concern over the potential increases in water charges (ref. 9). They have made it clear that in preparing asset management plans for the period beyond 1995 (AMP2) meeting existing and new statutory requirements be they EC or domestic must take priority over achieving the non-statutory RQOs.

48. It is also being proposed that in relation to the objective of preventing deterioration, the base-line will be taken as 1990 river quality and that expenditure to restore quality will only be permitted where there has been a subsequent deterioration.

49. These two constraints are likely to limit environmental improvements achieved in the Trent catchment over the next few years. Furthermore, 1990 is not a very appropriate year to use as a base-line for determining future expenditure. In each of the previous five years there had been a net downgrading of river quality. It has only been since 1990, as a result of Severn Trent's AMP1 expenditure to achieve RQOs that there has been an overall improvement in river quality.

Fishery Issues

50. Although the Trent and its tributaries are probably now better than for many decades in terms of traditional measures of water quality, this is not always perceived to be the case by the general public. A particular problem is the apparent decline of the lower Trent as a fishery which has been widely publicised, particularly in the local and angling press. It is difficult to quantify any changes which have occurred and to attribute causes. Various suggestions have been made including the impact of treated effluents, low river flows during recent summers, the changed nature of the cleaner river with its reduced turbidity and increased clarity. Use of the river for power station cooling water has tended to raise the temperature of the river throughout the year but changes in the methods and patterns of power generation are reducing this effect and NRA has recently suggested that the resulting lower river temperatures may be affecting fish catches.

51. On a more encouraging note, the formerly fishless lower reaches of the river Tame now support fisheries which are popular venues with local anglers.

CONCLUSIONS

52. The preceding discussion has illustrated the dramatic improvements which occurred in the Trent catchment as a result of major investment in pollution control. Much of this improvement was due to the implementation of basic pollution control measures prior to the period in which formal quality objectives and EC Directives were introduced.

53. Since the implementation of the Control of Pollution Act 1974 and Water Act 1989 with their statutory requirements for public access to data and involvement in the setting of consents and quality objectives, considerable attention has been focused on achieving compliance with existing standards - with considerable success. This is particularly important to statutory water companies such as Severn Trent for which compliance assessment is widely used by the public, regulators and others as a measure of the Company's performance. Equally it is important to NRA to demonstrate its vigilance in enforcing existing consents.

54. This emphasis on compliance during a period when resources have often been limited has led to major investment in asset renewal to maintain compliance and current quality. Although there have been significant river quality improvements, this has to some extent been a period of consolidation.

55. Another reason for the less spectacular progress is the much improved base from which any further improvements will be measured. The improvements to date have brought significant benefits in terms of increased scope for various river uses, however, there is obviously potential for the law of diminishing returns to operate, making further improvements more difficult to justify. The Guidelines for AMP2 planning emphasise the importance of cost benefit justification for tighter standards.

56. Nevertheless significant targets remain to be achieved in the catchment, perhaps most notably further improvement of the Tame and Erewash to meet their RQOs. The timing of such improvements depends on the outcome of current discussions on the scope of the AMP2 programme and on how statutory WQOs are implemented.

57. The increasing likelihood of further use of the Trent for water resources will make it crucial to maintain river quality and may ultimately be the critical use in determining future quality requirements.

ACKNOWLEDGEMENTS
The authors are grateful to the Managing Director of Severn Trent Water Ltd and the Regional Manager of the National Rivers Authority Severn Trent Region for permission to present this paper. The views expressed in the paper are those of the authors and are not necessarily those of Severn Trent Water Ltd or the National Rivers Authority.

REFERENCES

1. HARKNESS N. The River Tame - A Short History of Water Pollution and Control within an Industrial River Basin. Water Science Technology,1982,vol. 14,153-165.
2. TRENT RIVER BOARD. Annual Report, 1961.
3. WARN A.E. The Trent Mathematical Model. In: JAMES A. (Ed) Mathematical Models in Water Pollution Control. Wiley, 1978.
4. BOX M.H. Water Reclamation and River Management in the Tame Basin. Water Pollution Control,1984,vol. 83,254-264.
5. SEVERN TRENT WATER AUTHORITY River Water Quality and Review of Discharge Consents, 1979.
6. NATIONAL RIVERS AUTHORITY. Proposals for Statutory Water Quality Objectives. NRA Water Quality Series No. 5, 1991.
7. DEPARTMENT OF ENVIRONMENT AND WELSH OFFICE. River Quality. The Government's Proposals: A Consultation Paper. 1992
8. The Water Share Offers. Prospectus. 1989,
9. DEPARTMENT OF ENVIRONMENT AND WELSH OFFICE. Water Charges the Quality Framework. 1993.

'Operation Seaclean' — an environmental achievement for Southern Water

R. CLAYTON, DMS, CEng, MICE, MIStructE, MIWEM, Technical Director, and
J. BIRCUMSHAW, BSc, CEng, MICE, Planning Manager, Southern Water
Services Ltd

SYNOPSIS. 'Operation Seaclean' is the title of Southern
Water's wastewater treatment works improvement programme
which will bring the designated bathing beaches up to the
standards required by the EC Bathing Waters Directive.
The paper first sets out the background to the Company
and then considers the legislation with which the new
works will comply. It examines the common factors in
relation to each scheme, and concludes with a regional
overview highlighting the principal features of the major
schemes. The appendices give a summary of the 'Operation
Seaclean' programme and set out the parameters of the two
principal Directives in a simplified format.

INTRODUCTION

1. Southern Water is one of the 10 Water and Sewerage
Plcs which were created under the Water Act 1989. The
Company's area extends across the South East of England,
covering the Counties of Hampshire, the Isle of Wight,
Sussex and Kent. It has a network of over 24 000Km of
sewers that collect wastewater from over 4.25M people,
which is increased in summer by a further 0.25M visitors.
The coastline extends for a distance in excess of 1 000Km
from Barton-On-Sea in Hampshire and The Solent, including
the Isle of Wight, along the English Channel and into the
Thames Estuary in the North, to Gravesend.

2. 'Operation Seaclean' is the Company's response to
the need for improving the bathing water quality to the
higher standards demanded by the public and, on their
behalf, by both the UK and European Governments. The
region contains around 30% of the Country's designated
bathing waters which will be required to meet EC
standards by the end of 1995. A list of the major
'Operation Seaclean' schemes and completion dates is
given in Appendix 1. Six of these schemes were affected
by the 'Patten Initiative' which anticipated the Urban
Wastewater Directive. Implementation of the UWWTD will
require further work, through to the year 2000 and
beyond.

COMPANY STRUCTURE

3.   Southern Water Services is the principal subsidiary of Southern Water Plc and provides water and wastewater services in Kent, Sussex, Hampshire and the Isle of Wight where there are separate Divisions each based on County boundaries and headed by a Director.

4.   The Engineering design function within the Group is undertaken by McDowells Ltd which comprises technical staff from the former Southern Water Authority together with other specialist skills acquired from the private sector.   In addition Coastal Wastewater Consultants Ltd has been established as a joint venture in conjunction with the Mott MacDonald Group.

5.   Many of the environmental studies are undertaken by Southern Science Ltd.   Southern Science is the specialist scientific services subsidiary of Southern Water Plc and has the expertise to carry out a wide range of environmental studies which are an essential part of the planning process for major new works.

6.   Other major external Consultants are also being used to undertake major schemes within 'Operation Seaclean'.

THE LEGISLATIVE BACKGROUND

7.   The Council of the European Community has issued a number of Directives concerned with maintaining and improving the marine environment, all of which need to be taken into account with 'Operation Seaclean'.

8.   Bathing Water Directive (1976).   The Directive defines the water quality standards for bathing and requires periodic sampling and analysis.   Standards are expressed for total and faecal coliforms together with sampling frequency and compliance.   (Appendix 2).

9.   Dangerous Substances Directive (1976).   The Directive requires that member states should eliminate the pollution of waters by List I substances and reduce pollution by List II substances.   List I substances are selected on the basis of their toxicity, persistence and bio-accumulation in the marine environment (eg. mercury, cadmium) List II substances are those which might have a deleterious effect on the environment (eg. organic compounds of silicon).

10.   Shellfish Water Directive (1979).   The Directive defines water quality standards in terms of dissolved oxygen, suspended solids, salinity and faecal coliforms - it is not intended to be a measure to protect public health nor to ensure that shellfish are fit for direct sale or consumption.

11. <u>The Shellfish Hygiene Directive (1991)</u>. The
Directive was implemented in the UK in January 1993 and
defines the conditions required for the harvesting and
handling of shellfish to safeguard public health. Four
classes of shellfish quality are defined in relation to
water quality.

12. <u>The Urban Wastewater Directive (1991)</u>. The
Directive requires treatment of wastewater before
discharge, the appropriate level of which depends on the
size of the catchment population and the sensitivity of
the receiving water. (Appendix 3).

13. In 1991 the Company was invited by Chris Patten
(then Secretary of State for the Environment) to nominate
a number of schemes which would be carried out as part of
'Operation Seaclean', but would also comply with the
requirements of the then Draft Municipal Wastewater
Directive (now the Urban Wastewater Directive). These
became known as Patten Initiative schemes and are due for
completion by the end of 1995. They are indicated in
Appendix 1, but it should be noted that in some cases two
individual wastewater treatment works have been combined
into one scheme.

14. In addition to the foregoing Directives, there is a
need to comply with other European and UK legislation,
during the progression of a scheme. However, the most
significant of these from the 'Operation Seaclean'
viewpoint are the Bathing Water Directive and the Urban
Wastewater Directive together with the associated
Planning legislation.

THE DESIGN & CONSTRUCTION APPROACH

15. Each Division of Southern Water Services has
appointed Project Managers from within their own staff,
and project teams have been formed which comprise
in-house specialists, together with external Planning
Consultants who are seen as being professionally
independent by the Local Planning Authorities. Although
the 'Operation Seaclean' programme involves the
construction of many new wastewater treatment works,
there are a number of common factors which have to be
considered in relation to each scheme, and the general
studies which are undertaken are set out in the following
paragraphs.

16. <u>Land Based Studies</u>. New wastewater treatment works
generally have to be located in sensitive foreshore or
sea front locations due to the historical layout of
sewerage systems and therefore tend to be considered as
unwelcome neighbours. The planning work associated with
a new scheme is therefore a key issue and many new
'Operation Seaclean' proposals are subject to a detailed
Environmental Assessment.

17.   When considering the design of the wastewa⌐
treatment works, pumping, standby generation and
control facilities are usually required in additi
the treatment units.   Part or all the structures
to be underground due to their sensitive location
thereby requiring the provision of ventilation sy
gas monitoring and explosion protection of electr
equipment.

18.   Various odour control systems are being used by the
Company.   Wet scrubbing of the air by ozone and other
chemicals have been successful but are expensive both in
terms of capital and revenue.   Palletised bio-filters
using cheap, locally available media are likely to prove
a simple and cost effective solution for some future
schemes.

19.   The external appearance of a wastewater treatment
works needs to be treated sympathetically to ensure that
the building blends satisfactorily into its landscape.
Amenity use of the roof areas may be incorporated in the
finished scheme.

20.   Alteration to the sewerage systems to concentrate
flows at the new wastewater treatment works will nearly
always be required, as will extensive flow simulation
modelling of contributing catchments.   The abandonment or
upgrading of unsatisfactory storm overflows and storage
and flow control of storm water will usually be a part of
the overall design of a wastewater treatment scheme.

21.   The new works can be extensive involving major
pipelaying, tunnelling and construction of underground
tanks, frequently in congested urban areas.

22.   Marine Based Studies.   In many cases, the location
of an outfall will be fixed by the configuration of the
existing sewerage system, or by the presence of an
existing outfall which may be serviceable for further
use.   In other instances, however, a new outfall will be
required and the process of selecting the most suitable
site must be undertaken.

23.   The design process is a combination of desk
studies, mathematical modelling using sophisticated
software and field studies to assess current movements
and bacterial dispersion and die off periods, together
with an investigation into the nature of the sea bed both
in terms of its physical characteristics to support the
construction and service life of the outfall and also the
ecology of the area.

24.   The following steps are required:-
      * A literature search for previous relevant
         information - a considerable amount of data is
         usually available.

* The use of Admiralty charts and tide tables to
assess water depths and initial current movements.
It is necessary to locate the diffuser section in
suitable depths of water (depending on local
currents) at low water spring tides to obtain
appropriate initial dilution at the end of the
outfall depending upon local circumstances and
levels of treatment proposed.

25. These studies identify likely outfall locations and
discharge sites plus early estimates as to length
required. They also show:-

* Current movements over the full tidal cycles.
* Physical obstructions, restricted areas,
fishing grounds, navigation routes, etc.
* Planning constraints.

26. Field Studies. These are usually necessary to
confirm the results of the theoretical work. Field
verification is carried out by the use of radar
techniques, dye tracing and float tracking studies and by
monitoring controlled releases of tracer bacteria or
spores.

27. The effects of wind on currents can be simulated in
the computer model using local meteorological data.

28. The combinations of these studies assists in the
selection of one or two suitable discharge locations
whereby satisfactory dilution and dispersion takes place
and bacterial die-off occurs sufficiently far from
bathing waters to ensure compliance with the Bathing
Water Directive.

THE MAJOR SCHEMES UNDERTAKEN

29. Appendix 1 sets out a comprehensive list of the
major projects which together comprise 'Operation
Seaclean'. Taken together, they form a group of schemes
which demonstrate engineering skills of a high order. In
this paper it is not possible to give full details of
each scheme, although some of the more interesting
aspects of the major works are summarised below.

30. In Hampshire the new Pennington WTW (£9M) will be
constructed below the level of the adjacent ground in a
borrow pit at present being excavated by the NRA for
material to construct a new sea wall. There were severe
planning constraints to be overcome as almost all the
coastline around Pennington is within a Site of Special
Scientific Interest. The land adjacent to the site of
the new works is designated as an Area of Outstanding
Natural Beauty. Inland, the New Forest Heritage Area is
to have National Park status and other areas are
protected wetlands or nature reserves.

31. A full environmental assessment was carried out prior to submitting the planning application. It is intended that the new works will provide effluent treatment to secondary standard using compact units.

32. Due to difficulties of access, the Fawley scheme (£4M) is now likely to comprise the construction of a pumping station and rising main which will transfer the flow under Southampton Water. This will utilise a tunnel previously constructed by the National Grid for power transmission cables and the sewage will be treated at the Company's major wastewater treatment works at Peel Common, Fareham. This particular scheme is a good example of the co-operation which is now possible between privatised Utility Companies.

33. The Portsmouth scheme (£20M) was designed to serve a population of 180 000 and comprises preliminary treatment and storm water storage. Its major feature is a new sea outfall 1.4m diameter and 5.7Km in length which is one of the longest in the UK.

34. On the Isle of Wight a new headworks providing preliminary treatment and a long sea outfall has been constructed to serve the town of Ryde (£10M). The headworks were contained in a building on the Esplanade which subsequently gained an architectural award. On the western side of the Island, the Yarmouth wastewater scheme will include a directionally drilled crossing of the River Yar; an example of how technology developed for oil field exploration can be utilised to good effect in other applications.

35. In Kent, the largest scheme of the 'Operation Seaclean' series has now been re-submitted to the Local Planning Authority. Initially, the Planning Application for the scheme which had evolved with the co-operation of the Local Councils was submitted to the Folkestone Borough Council for approval, and was unexpectedly rejected. This led to considerable delays whilst a re-appraisal was undertaken, but the revised scheme and associated environmental statement is now with the Kent County Council for determination. The Dover/Folkestone scheme (£120M) comprises a new underground wastewater treatment works for 140 000 population, five new pumping stations and over four kilometres of new sewers and tunnels. The new treatment works which is situated in an Area of Outstanding National Beauty will serve both towns. Effluent will be discharged through a new sea outfall 2.5Km in length.

36. Another major project in Kent is the Richborough scheme (£38M) which will provide a new wastewater treatment works at Weatherlees Hill, to serve the Ramsgate, Sandwich and Deal areas. The effluent will receive secondary treatment before discharge into the River Stour. Also in Kent, the Herne Bay wastewater treatment scheme (£24M) will stop the discharge of untreated wastewater into the sea and provide a treated effluent for discharge into the River Stour. This will augment river flows and sustain the operation of a water abstraction and treatment plant downstream.

37. The Sussex Division has five major schemes which together form part of 'Operation Seaclean'. The Brighton/Hove stormwater scheme (£36M) has been designed to increase stormwater capacity by providing a tunnel 6m diameter and 5Km in length at an average depth of 35m below the shore. The tunnel will intercept existing storm overflow discharges from outfalls and retain flows for pumping to the treatment works at Portobello once the storm subsides thus reducing the frequency of storm discharges to sea. The project will also provide an amenity building at the Black Rock Pumping Station site.

38. The new Worthing Wastewater Treatment Scheme (£37M) has been designed to replace existing out of date facilities with a modern treatment works and a new sea outfall 4.5Km long. There will also be a new stormwater outfall 1Km in length. A similar scheme is being constructed in Eastbourne (£45.9M) where a new sea outfall 3.2Km is already in place. Preliminary and primary treatment to the effluent will be given in a new underground works incorporating odour control. The works access building will be constructed to have the appearance of a Napoleonic Fort.

39. A scheme for the Shoreham area (£24M) is also being proposed as part of 'Operation Seaclean'. This will involve a new wastewater treatment works on the southern side of Shoreham Harbour together with a new sea outfall 3.1Km in length and 760mm in diameter.

CONCLUSION

40. 'Operation Seaclean' is now approaching the halfway stage and is due to be completed by the end of 1995. At this time Southern Water will have invested £450M in over forty separate schemes comprising a large number of new treatment works, at least ten new long sea outfalls and the replacement of many shorter outfalls which no longer comply with current legislation.

41. 'Operation Seaclean' is collectively the largest programme of new works ever carried out by the Company and will become an outstanding Environmental achievement. However, the cost of the work undertaken in this major programme is significantly less than the next series of projects which will be to enhance many of the Company's wastewater treatment works and to implement a strategy for disposing of increasing amounts of sewage sludge as required by the Urban Wastewater Directive. Southern Water will therefore be moving forward with confidence as the lessons learnt from 'Operation Seaclean' in the planning and execution of major projects are put into practice to meet the increasing standards required by continuing legislation.

OPERATION SEACLEAN

The following is a summary of the major projects which together form Operation Seaclean. These include associated sewerage elements.

Location		Anticipated Completion	Status
* Barton transfer to Pennington and Pennington WWTW	(H)	1995	Pennington WWTW – Planning Application for Autumn 1993
Fawley	(H)	1994/95	Under design
Portsmouth (Eastney)	(H)	1991/92	Complete
Bembridge	(IOW)	1994/95	Planning approval obtained for pumping station for transfer to Sandown
Cowes	(IOW)	1991/92	Complete
Totland	(IOW)	1993/94	In progress
Yarmouth	(IOW)	1993/94	In progress
Ventnor	(IOW)	1995	Planning approval obtained. Contract documents in preparation
Ryde	(IOW)	1990/91	Complete
* Dover/ Folkestone	(K)	1996/97	Revised Planning Application submitted August/Sept 1993
Herne Bay	(K)	1994/95	Contracts shortly to be awarded. Consents received
* Ramsgate/ Sandwich/ Deal (Weatherlees Hill)	(K)	1994/95	Under construction

Location		Anticipated Completion	Status
Whitstable	(K)	1993/94	Under construction
Brighton/Hove (Stormwater Storage)	(S)	1997	Under construction
* Shoreham	(S)	1995	Tenders received. Awaiting NRA consent
* Worthing	(S)	1994/95	Under construction
Newhaven/ Seaford	(S)	1992/93	Completed
* Eastbourne	(S)	1995	Under construction

| | Total | £450 million | |

* Indicates 'Patten Initiative' scheme.
(H) Hampshire Division
(IOW) Isle of Wight Division
(K) Kent Division
(S) Sussex Division

In addition to these projects which are either completed or ongoing, the new generation of schemes to comply with the Urban Wastewater Directive are being developed. The Government has yet to inform Water Companies of the detailed interpretation of the Directive, and hence the level of treatment which will be required.

EC BATHING WATERS DIRECTIVE

*   The NRA is the regulatory body.

*   This Directive sets standards for designated bath
        waters including:-

        - total coliforms < 10 000 per 100 ml

        - faecal coliforms < 2 000 per 100 ml

        - sampling according to the specified programme
          between the months of May and September.

*   95% compliance is required according to the
        look-up table.

APPENDIX 3

EC URBAN WASTEWATER DIRECTIVE –
SPECIFICATION IN ASCENDING LEVELS OF TREATMENT

Population Equivalent	Receiving Water	Specified Treatment	Deadline End Of
>150 000	Areas of high natural dispersion	Secondary or Primary *	2000
	Normal	Secondary	2000
	Sensitive	Secondary +	1998
15 000 – 150 000	Areas of high natural dispersion	Primary	2000
	Normal	Secondary	2000
	Sensitive	Secondary +	1998
2 000 – 10 000	Normal coastal waters	Appropriate	2005
	Areas of high natural dispersion Estuaries	Primary	2005
	Other Estuaries and Freshwater	Secondary	2005
<2 000	All receiving waters	Appropriate	2005

Notes: Primary * indicates that this form of treatment is acceptable in exceptional circumstances.

Secondary + indicates that N&P removal may be required.

Developing a strategy for environmental improvements in a major European river

D. W. RODDA, OBE, MICE, FIWEM, Team Leader, Danube Programme Coordination Unit, Commission of European Communities, Brussels

SYNOPSIS. The Environmental Programme of the Danube River Basin has the objective to establish an operational basis for strategic and integrated management of the Danube basin environment focusing on priority issues. Due to time constraints the paper is brief, but it introduces some of the character of the Danube catchment, explains some of the problems being faced, and explores some of the strategy points in order to prepare for the drafting of a strategic action plan with particular reference to municpal wastewater treatment.

INTRODUCTION

1. Within the range of assistance programmes for Central and Eastern Europe, a particular programme has been established known as the Environmental Programme for the Danube River Basin. It is an example of a regional initiative providing a focus on and the development of action to reverse the impact of the environmental degradation that has occurred basin-wide and the pollution which is transferred from one country to another by the river flowing downstream to the Delta, the largest in Europe, and then to the Black Sea.

2. The Environmental Programme for the Danube River basin is steered by a Task Force on which are represented all the riparian countries, the main International Financing Institutions (Commission of the European Communities (CEC), UN/Global Environment Facility (GEF)-involved partners are UNDP which manages GEF, The World Bank, UNEP-European Bank for Reconstruction and Development, European Investment Bank) and a representative group of internationally-based NGO Institutions such as the Worldwide Fund for Nature, World Conservation Union, Regional Environment Centre for Central and Eastern Europe, and, recently agreed, a locally based NGO group. Equipe Cousteau has made a substantial contribution to the Programme. The day-to-day action on the Programme is coordinated by a Programme Coordination Unit based temporarily in Brussels. The 2 largest funders of the Programme are the CEC at 13.4 million ecus and the GEF at 7.1 million ecus.

3. The Danube is the second largest river in Europe with a catchment area of 817,000 km², covering the whole or part of more than 11 countries. Its source is in Germany and it enters the Black Sea via a Delta, the largest wetland in Europe. Transboundary impact is therefore of major concern in the region.

4. The Delta covers more than 550,000 ha of rivers, lakes, reedswamp, meadows and primary forest is rich in fish and is a unique ecosystem. Its survival is threatened by a variety of activities which include the transport of pollution, the degree of canalisation and the reduction in the sediment loads resulting from the construction of dams in the river upstream. Over 300,000 ha of the Delta is a Biosphere Reserve and part is listed under the Ramsar Convention and over half of its area is on the World Heritage list.

5. The Black Sea, particularly in the North-West shelf bordering the coastlines of Bulgaria, Romania, and Ukraine, is permanently anoxic below depths of 150 to 200 metres, and is regarded as one of the most seriously degraded of the world's seas.

6. Most of the Programme activity over the last 12-15 months, now at a halfway stage, has been to identify and quantify, where possible, the extent of the environmental degradation that has taken place, to assess the needs of Institutional Development and the priorities for action. This paper, as a contribution to the Conference, therefore provides a brief account of the municipal wastewater treatment facilities in the Danube basin, and the considerations that are being applied to the selection of priorities, options for immediate and strategic action and the constraints that apply. These comments are in the context of other forms of pollution namely industrial wastes disposal and activities giving rise to diffuse pollution e g agriculture and variety of environmental degradation.

ASSOCIATED INSTITUTIONAL DEVELOPMENTS

7. The Danube riparian countries are negotiating a new Convention on Cooperation for the Protection and Sustainable Use of the Danube River. The provisions take account of those already included in the framework Convention on the Protection and Use of Transboundary Waters and International Lakes signed in Helsinki in March 1992. Most Danube riparian countries signed the Convention. The negotiations for the new Danube Convention have been led by Austria and it has been agreed that signing will take place in 1994. Another draft Convention has been proposed by Hungary to address the concern over the protection of ecosystems, but the negotiations are proceeding slowly and there is at present no clear indication when they will be completed.

8. Subject to the riparian countries of the Danube basin ratifying the Austrian-led Convention and it enters into force, there is the prospect of appropriate legislation for dealing with many of the concerns in the basin being available for application in each country.

9.   Another focus on dealing with the environmental degradation is provided by the Environmental Action Programme for Central and Eastern Europe which was adopted by the Pan-European Conference of Environment Ministers in Lucerne from 28 to 30 April 1993.   This Programme places main emphasis on further capacity for strengthening capabilities, institutional building, training to improve environmental management; developing a realistic legislative and regulatory framework for the environment; sound policy development; and the setting of appropriate priorities to reduce emissions. By its title this Programme is concerned with all the countries in Central and Eastern Europe and it may be that the riparian countries of the Danube basin, by their concerted action over the Austrian-led draft Convention, are making faster progress with the action required.

MUNICIPAL WASTEWATER TREATMENT FACILITIES

10. In keeping with the theme of the Conference there is much of concern to be addressed in respect of municipal wastewater treatment facilities. A variety of studies have been carried out to identify the major pollution problems from point-source discharges to tributaries of the Danube main river.   The tributaries were selected because initial assessments indicated that it was the surface waters in these catchments which suffer the worst impacts from point source pollution. A total of 17 tributaries have been studied with catchments in the Czech Republic, Slovak Republic, Slovenia, Hungary, Bulgaria, Romania, Moldova and Ukraine. Some of these are transboundary waters such as the Siret and Drava rivers, the two largest Danube tributaries.

11.   The problems associated with the 1000s of existing municipal wastewater disposal facilities recorded in the pre-investment studies and other Programme reports, range from the complete lack of any treatment through a variety of part treatment to at least secondary treatment. Many discharges are of raw sewage direct into the rivers. In many cases the facilities require extensive overhaul or replacement. Often the discharges contain a mixture of domestic and industrial wastes, the latter being as much as 50% or even more of the volume. There is particular concern over these combined discharges because any approach to treat the waste would have to deal with high levels of metals, micropollutants and oil residues in many cases. Many townships do not have sewerage and the prospect of new sewers leading to larger flows to be treated raises further questions about the priorities.

12.   An obvious solution for dealing with the problem of combined discharges is to control the pollution at source and apply the Best Available Technology (BAT). Such a policy has been well applied in the European Community, but its application in the Danube basin requires new legislation, changed responsibilities for National and Municipal Institutions, and a major injection of funding principally from the countries themselves. In addition

any option for tackling the situation has to take account of the viability of industries whose discharges require regulation and control. Therefore it is not only a question of finding the best technical solutions.

SETTING PRIORITIES FOR A STRATEGY

13.   This brief account of the problems of dealing with municipal wastewater treatment, and within the wider context of all point and non-point source pollution in the Danube basin leads to the consideration of a range of options for arriving at a preferred strategy. Central to this is the need to agree the objectives for any strategy. Currently proposals for these are a matter for consultation in the basin: it is considered that these are of at least 2 types:

Functional e g protection of ecosystems, safeguarding health; prevention and control of pollution at source

Geographical e g international as compared with national

14.   There are several issues to be discussed in the context of these objectives.   Protection of water resources; the efficient prevention, reduction and control of non-point source pollution; the protection of fisheries; the provision of a system for preventing accidental pollution; and impacts on ecosystems are some of these. Alongside these there is a need to address the improvements needed in environmental management-legislation, economics and financial management including the issue of paying for the services, institutions and their responsibilities, and staff capabilities and training.   Processes which will lead towards the implementation of integrated resources management within the context of river basin management appropriate to each country, will need to be addressed.

15.   International or National Priorities. The question of the emphasis on the international or transboundary aspects compared with the national and local aspects is a matter which will require careful attention. It is already becoming clear because of the serious eutrophic state of the northwest shelf zone of the Black Sea, that action will be needed to reduce the loads of nutrients entering the Sea from the rivers draining into it. The Danube is claimed to be the largest contributor and estimates indicate that some 600,000 tons of phosphorus and 340,000 of inorganic nitrogen enter each year into the Sea.

16.   The question here is what level of target should be set on which to plan a strategy. At one of the meetings a reduction of 50% in the nutrient load discharged to the Black Sea was rejected as being impracticable, on account of the extent of the works required in many countries and the cost involved. Also scientists seem undecided whether N or P is limiting in the Black Sea. Other targets discussed range from; no improvement in N and P; through a variety of %s to say 25%.

17. The challenge is that if the improvement in the quality of the Black Sea is to be a target, however defined, then 10% or 25% reduction in the River basin may not be enough.

18. Many groundwater supplies are also affected by raised levels of nitrate and evidence is given in the Environmental Action Plan for Central and Eastern Europe of a marked incidence of Methemoglobinemia in the Danube countries of the Slovak Republic, Hungary, Bulgaria, and Romania.

19. On the other hand there is concern over the extent of bacteriological contamination of the surface waters from untreated wastewaters which is regarded more of a national problem associated with the level of treatment provided and the siting of point-source discharges.

20. Another issue that may be regarded as a basin-wide problem requiring a priority assessment is the transport of sediments and activities which influence the transport, and which facilitates the movement of adsorbed organic compounds downstream, particularly those which are toxic, persistent and bioaccumulative. There may be other issues.

21. Standard Setting. The selection of standards either those for controlling emissions or as ambient standards will be another consideration. In the case of emission standards for municipal wastewaters, countries seeking to improve control over polluting discharges are likely to want to set standards to match those set in European Community Directives, especially where they would be more stringent than they have in their present legislation. A policy for Central and Eastern European countries has been established in that for all new investments CEC standards should be applied even if the project lifetime is calculated to be for 15-20 years. European agreements containing clauses to this effect-obliging countries to work towards the CEC standards- have been signed by Czech Republic, Slovak Republic, Hungary, Romania and Bulgaria. An agreement is being negotiated with Slovenia. The purpose here is to establish 'a level playing field' in relation to marketing and trade. Programmes for improving the effluent quality need to take this policy into account when preparing projects and estimating costs.

22. Harmonisation of Standards. In the case of the Danube catchment where there are several countries affected by transboundary pollution, the harmonisation of standards may seem attractive. It is referred to more than once in the new Convention. Such a strategy has cost implications and a study recently completed by the European Bank for Reconstruction and Development entitled 'Environmental Standards and Legislation in Central and Eastern Europe: Towards Harmonisation', in cooperation with the CEC, included a case study on the Danube catchment, and addressed this point. The report's main conclusion on the Danube study is 'The scale of investment needed for harmonisation of sewage effluent standards is large and will result in substantial cost increases for sewerage services.'

23. 'Hot-spot Priorities'. The selection of pollution 'hot-spots' represents another level of debate in the overall selection of priorities for establishing a

strategy. It has been explained above that several tributary basins have been selected for assessment and the experts who made the assessments used a variety of criteria to establish the prioritiy 'hot-spots'. To a large extent the basic criteria relied on estaimates of the polluting load and its effect on the receiving waters. The challenge in many instances is whether the criteria could be extended to enable an improved assessment to be made of the effects on the environment and on human health. Thus an assessment heirarchy could be set on the following basis, each level of analysis being more demanding:

> end of pipe/emission load discharged

> effect on receiving waters e g surface water quality classification

> environmental impact e g to include effects on flora, fauna and habitats

> health impact e g through a variety of water uses such as for drinking water supply

Most experts have adopted the emission load approach combined with the effect on receiving waters because of the lack of data to go further, but an assessment made in this way may not provide for the most critical 'hot-spot'.
24. Another approach which might be said to be an academic one in the case of the Danube rivers because of the lack of data, uses a risk assessment analysis based on a model used by the United States Environment Protection Agency (USEPA). Here much effort has to be assigned in establishing the health concern of a particular polluting activity. This type of analysis is much more demanding in time and effort by experts which was not usually allowed for in the contracts. The approach involves the following steps:

> identifying the hazard in terms of known effects on human health

> selecting the known dose response in humans

> quantifying the exposure e g location/population, timing/duration, fate, estimated human intake or exposure

> characterisation of the risk

> ranking the risk

Learning Resources
Centre

OPTIONS AND CONSTRAINTS IN STRATEGY DEVELOPMENT

25. An important consideration in developing a strategy is to ensure as far as possible that the strategy is realistic. The International Financing Institutions are not able to meet all the investment costs and there needs to be an acceptance by the countries that they themselves will have to pay for or raise from local resources most of the funds required. The 'lowest common denominator' approach should be avoided wherever possible. There are usually a variety of options and there are constraints; the Danube basin is no exception especially as there are 11 countries participating in the Programme.

26. Some of the options are:

Change in emphasis on planned rate of improvement between countries. This may not be an acceptable option because the Conventions have been negotiated to prevent,reduce or control transboundary pollution.

Development of decentralisation whereby municipalities, regional bodies take responsibility for waste management in their area and may delegate part of their responsibility to private companies. There are many models of decentralisation.

Achieving local improvements in water services by either reducing the cost of services, particularly use of energy and materials: improving the standard of service based on improved management efficiency; expand services again centering on better organisational structure and capabilities.

Cost recovery measures which could include metering (many townships do not pay for water but the low income of people may pose a challenge); the reduction of water consumption (rates as high as 400 litres per head per day are known); and better financial management and administration.

CONCLUSION

27. The Danube main river flows through the heart of Europe and is a strategic waterway joining countries with market-based economies with those which have for over 40 years had centralist economies. The river possesses a beauty which is crowned by the largest river delta in Europe over half the area of which has been placed on the World Heritage list. It is seriously threatened by severe pollution and a major effort is currently being made to establish a comprehensive strategy to reduce the degradation. A Strategic Action Plan is to be prepared for the River Basin Programme starting in the first part of 1994. There are many targets and options to be assessed for the plan, but its drafting will provide a unique challenge to

those involved. Implementation of the Plan will lie mainly with those having responsibility in the basin for environmental matters, and guided, with their agreement, by a variety of International Institutions who are prepared to make their expertise available under a range of aid agreements.

ACKNOWLEDGEMENTS

28. The contribution made to the Programme by the members of the Task Force and the staff of the Programme Co-ordination Unit and the many consultants and experts providing reports containing advice and the results of needs assessment studies are gratefully acknowledged. The paper represents the views of the author and does not represent the views of the Commission of the European Communities or any other Task Force member.

REFERENCES

1. Environmental Action Programme for Central and Eastern Europe. (1993). Document submitted to the Ministerial Conference Lucerne, Switzerland.

2. Convention on the Protection and Use of Transboundary Watercourses and International Lakes. (1992). Signed in Helsinki.

3. Saving the Black Sea. (1993). Booklet published by the United Nations Development Programme, United Nations Environment Programme and The World Bank. Copyright by the World Bank.

4. European Community Environment Legislation. Volume 7 Water. Published by the Commission of the European Communities, Directorate General X1, Environment, Nuclear Safety and Civil Protection.

Sewage treatment for small communities — the Severn Trent approach

J. E. UPTON, BSc, FIWEM, Process Development Manager,
M. B. GREEN, BSc, MIBiol, MIWEM, Principal Process Development
Scientist, and G. E. FINDLAY, BSc, LLB, MICE, MIWEM, Principal Engineer
(Small Works), Severn Trent Water Limited

SYNOPSIS. The paper presents an approach to small works design and operation developed in one of the UK water companies. Design selection considerations are based on consent conditions, population and cost for sewage works treating populations less than 2000 pe, the preferred flow sheet is RBC unit followed by a reed bed system. Data are provided for installation and operating costs and some comparison is made with alternative systems. Quality data from RBC and reed bed installations and from a storm reed bed system during a storm event are presented.

INTRODUCTION

1. A convenient sizing for small works is provided in the E.C. Urban Waste Water Directive. The directive defines baseline consent conditions for agglomerations greater than 2,000 population equivalent. For lesser populations it requires that appropriate treatment is provided. Member states are free to set discharge consents which are more restrictive than the baselines established by the directive.

2. Severn Trent Water Ltd. supplies water to and treats effluent from about 8 million customers and as a consequence is a major operator of sewage treatment facilities. The company operates in the order of 1050 wastewater plants of which about 75% are classified as small sewage works serving populations of less than 2000.

3. Most of these small works at the time of privatisation of the water companies were suffering from lack of investment and many were in poor structural condition. A wide range of plants had been in operation, the majority being traditional bacteria bed works, but a small number of prefabricated package type aeration units were in use together with a similar number of more recent installations comprising rotating biological contactors (RBCs).

4. The performance of these small works had deteriorated with many of the facilities failing to meet discharge consents; the level of compliance had fallen to 65%, and consents were in the process of being tightened. The company was faced with a strategic requirement to replace many of these ageing assets which were also proving a cost burden because of high

maintenance and attendance, a decision was taken to replace 100 small treatment works over a two year period with an ongoing programme of replacement thereafter. The pace of this programme of investment and construction demanded a streamlined approach and the normal site by site evaluation and procurement procedures were superceded by a process design matrix.

5. Basically process flow sheets were developed into a two dimensional matrix which focused the choice of process related to the desired effluent quality and size of works. A design matrix was established for medium to large works (2,000 to 50,000 pe) and a separate matrix for small works (< 2000 pe). This concept and some of the details of the approach has been described by Crabtree and Rowell (ref 1).

PROCESS SELECTION

6. A wide variety of consents were in force at the small works within Severn Trent but, in common with other areas of the UK, the salient parameters of concern were BOD and suspended solids (SS) with an increasing number of small works requiring to remove ammoniacal nitrogen (amm.N) as consents tightened to achieve River Quality Objectives. It is worth noting that in certain of the other EC member states (Germany, Holland and more recently Belgium) works below 2000 pe are frequently required to remove nutrients (N&P) before discharge, but this remains a potential future scenario for the UK.

7. For small works in Severn Trent an RBC is selected and where the discharge consent is tighter than 25 mg BOD/l and 45 mg SS/l a reed bed system is added.

8. A number of the very smallest of the works (<250 pe) are covered by descriptive consents and for the smallest of these (<50 pe) Severn Trent's preferred approach is to install a septic tank arrangement followed by a reed bed. Reviews of the design and performance of a septic tank and reed bed installation at Little Stretton (Leics.) has been described previously (ref. 2 and 3) and the authors will confine their attention in this paper to the RBC and reed bed initiative.

Rotating Biological Contactor

9. Prefabricated RBC plant currently available in the U.K. fall into two broad groups:-

    i,   Integral Units
    ii,   Modular Units

10. Integral Units. A typical integral unit is shown in Fig. 1.

11. In these designs the primary, secondary oxidation units and settlement clarifier are all housed under one cover. The accumulated sludge is removed at 2 or 3 monthly intervals by tankers and transported to sludge digestion centres for processing. The unit is totally enclosed, odour free; environmentally sympathetic and, when telemetry is incorporated to relay

warning of power failure or breakdown, the only essential visits required are to remove the sludge. However, the largest integral unit reliably capable of producing a well nitrified effluent can serve only about 250 people for larger populations up to four units can be installed in parallel with the flow split equally between each unit.

12. <u>Modular Units</u>. These are used where the equivalent population exceeds 1000 and or infiltration is high. The flow sheet is similar to that of a bacteria bed works except that the filter bed is replaced by the RBC unit. The inlet is not provided with separate screens and grit removal.

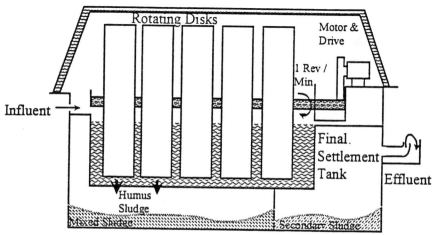

Fig. 1 Cross sectional of a typical rotating biological contactor.

13. Experience with RBC plant in Severn Trent has determined the design loadings necessary for these units to achieve full treatment and importantly 95%ile compliance with consents. These disc loadings have been explained by Crabtree and Rowell (ref.1) and are lower and more conservative than some of the loading values employed for designs elsewhere in Europe where the discharge permit may be based on an 80%ile compliance, reflecting, a more relaxed regulatory situation.

Problem Areas

14. Severn Trent experience with RBC installations has historically demonstrated a number of operational difficulties including:-

> inadequate sized primary tanks;
> poor final clarifier performance;
> failure of rotor shafts;
> failure of walls between primary and final tanks;
> sensitivity to high flow regimes;
> variable specification of ancillary equipment - spares problems.

The company has attempted to resolve a number of these problems by careful specification. In addition, Severn Trent's concern over some of the structural constraints and weaknesses was sufficient for the company to develop a prototype integral RBC capable of treating flows from 500 pe. This has operated successfully since March 1992.

15. This new design of RBC incorporates a number of unique features, not least the design of a rotor and shaft assembly designed to withstand some of the resultant stresses imposed by the rotation of the shaft and media assembly within the reactor. This feature and others are described by Findlay and Bannister (ref. 4). The RBC is being developed for production and will resolve some of the current problems of splitting small flows by extending the range of integral units from 1000 to 2000 pe.

Flows to full treatment

16. Many of the small treatment works replaced during the company's asset renewal programme treated all flows arriving at the works, sometimes with associated flooding during severe storms. Others, being small scale copies of larger works, were provided with storm tanks and separate outfalls for storm sewage. Earlier work surveying RBC performance had clearly identified excess flows as being a process problem so the decision was made to limit flow to full treatment to 6 dwf (6 pe + I + 3E).

17. In some cases the regulator had no objection to the direct discharge of these excess flows after fine screening but, in other cases, the response varied from acceptance of no stormwater discarge to the setting of numerical consents akin to those for storm tank effluents.

Separation of flows

18. Many of the small catchments with combined, or partially separate systems, have extreme variations in flow during storm conditions. The relatively small 6 x DWF in such cases makes conventional side weirs incapable of providing accurate storm separation. An effective method of dealing with this problem uses an orifice at the inlet to the biozone of the RBC regulating the flows over weirs in an adjacent chamber (ref. 5).

Treatment of storm overflows

19. Where treatment is required, screened storm water is fed onto constructed reed beds. The arrangement of the systems is partly dependent on the discharge consent constraints but the applications fit within the two extremes described in Fig. 2.

20. The reed beds are designed to accommodate the intermittent nature of the storm discharges with overflow arrangements provided to relieve the beds should the flows exceed about 12 DWF. At these extreme flows the reed beds still provide settlement and dilution. Green (ref. 6) calculates a retention time in the region of 7 hr at 12 DWF for a 1000 pe works.

Reed Beds

21. The design and operation of the tertiary treatment reed bed system has been described in some detail; by Green and Upton (refs 6 and 7) and the basic design is illustrated in Fig. 3. The company has improved this basic design approach and now, through successive refinements to the design of the inlet and outlet arrangements and reed establishment, the performance of these units is outstanding.

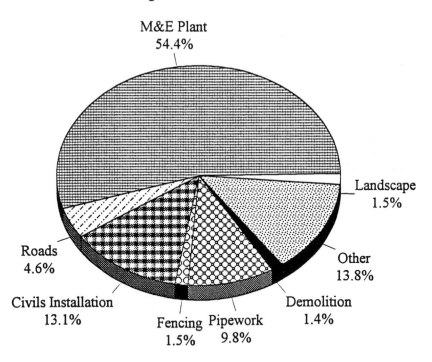

Fig. 2 Schematic arrangement for storm treatment reed bed at 2 typical discharge consent scenarios (reproduced with permission of WEF, Alexandria, USA ref. 6).

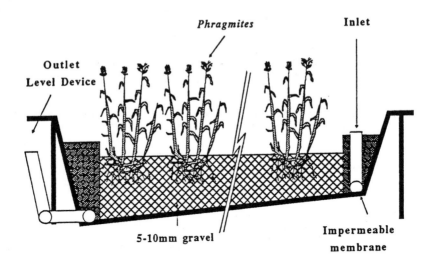

Fig. 3 Longtitudinal section of a typical constructed reed bed.

COSTS

 Capital Costs

22. Severn Trent have constructed in the order of 100 RBC and reed bed installations in the period 1991 - 1994. Analysis of the installed costs of these exhibits the variation that could be anticipated where individual existing site requirements have to be accommodated. However some useful information can be derived and Fig. 4 illustrates the cost analysis of RBC installation.

23. The largest proportion of the capital cost is of course associated with the electrical and mechanical component of the reactor; and the factor of organic loading on the disc has a significant effect. Two of the more widely used disc loading rates - 2.5 g BOD/ m^2d and 4.0 g BOD/m^2d day BOD reflect this effect with an increase in the M&E contract value by around 50% from the higher to lower loading figure.

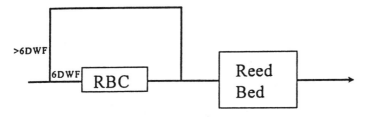

a) Discharge Consent 25mg BOD/l; 45 mg SS/l - No storm overflow consent

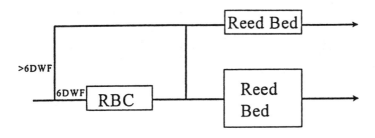

b) Discharge Consent 20 mg BOD/l; 30 mg ss/l, or tighter - treated storm overflow consented

Fig. 4 M&E and total costs for RBC schemes in Severn Trent Water

24. The cost of ancillaries such as fencing and site infrastructure varies greatly from site to site and specific installations; risks of vandalism and provision of tanker access are examples of factors which can affect these costs.

25. The use of the modular type of RBC installation has proved to be more expensive that the integral type of unit but the company expects to show savings at future sites where the new type of integral RBC can be utilised across a wider population range.

26. A profile of the capital cost per head of population is illustrated in Fig. 5.

27. The capital costs of reed beds is best illustrated by a comparison (Fig. 6) of the installed costs with those of modular sand filters, both systems offering a solution where effluent polishing is required (ref. 7).

28. The asset life of the reed bed systems is assumed to be around 20 years as sufficient free board is allowed for the accumulation of reed litter and effluent derived solids. Reed beds are cheaper to install at small works, than the modular sand filters which are more costly to operate and maintain and have an assumed asset life in order of 15 years.

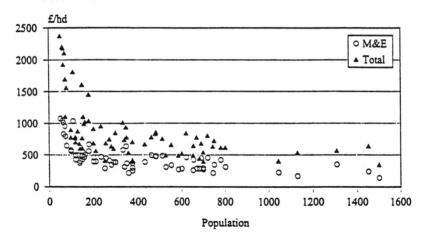

Fig. 5 M&E and total costs for RBC schemes in Severn Trent Water.

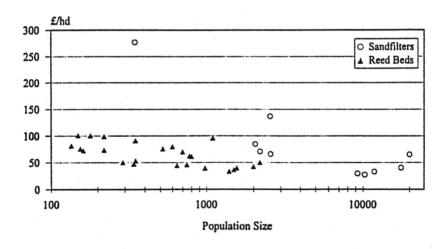

Fig. 6 Comparison between capital costs of tertiary treatment reed beds and modular sand filters for different population sizes.
(reproduced with permission of WEF, Alexandria USA ref. 7).

Revenue Costs

29. The compilation of operating cost data for small works has been difficult but Table 1 expresses the data obtained from 2 Districts within the company that were able to provide a breakdown of revenue costs. These costs included sludge tankering, supervision, power consumption and maintenance.

Table 1. Operating costs by treatment type

Sites		Population		Operating cost £/ hd. yr	
	No.	range	average	range	average
RBC	10	100-497	312	5.11 to 20.18	11.51
Percolating Filter	19	100-549	274	10.30 to 35.39	17.18

30. These costs illustrate the competitive advantage of the RBC initiative which exhibits approximately 30% lower costs per capita than the traditional bacteria bed sites. Furthermore it is expected that these RBC costs, which reflect the first generation of plants, will reduce as visiting frequencies are reviewed.

31. A important consideration of the RBC installation is that the rateable value for this type of flow sheet when compared with a traditional bacteria bed works is some 60% lower and this course will be reflected in lower revenue costs.

RBC + REED BED PERFORMANCE

32. The biggest challenge to small works is their ability consistently to meet consent conditions which are tighter than the 25 mg BOD/l and 35 mg SS/l requirement defined in the Urban Waste Water Directive; Fig. 7 illustrates the effectiveness of the RBC and reed bed combination in meeting that challenge. The final effluents from the more closely monitored works are little different from those at all of the sites where reed beds are used for effluent polishing.

33. Some RBCs, like those at Naseby are producing ultra high quality effluent which in part reflects a condition where the plant is some way short of it design loading. At the other end of the range of RBC performance, Lydbury North is an overloaded unit which is programmed for replacement and Himley is a site affected by trade discharges and the RBC unit produces highly nitrified effluent with very poor settlement characteristics.

34. Reed beds improve effluents in term of BOD and SS immediately on commissioning (ref. 7) and although improvement in amm.N removal takes time to establish; most sites show an improvement in their second year of operation. There was a benefit at all but one site shown in Fig. 7. At this site a high loading of solids and associated organic nitrogen caused an elevation

83

in ammoniacial nitrogen. This increase has no influence on compliance with consent conditions and is showing signs of diminishing as the system becomes further established.

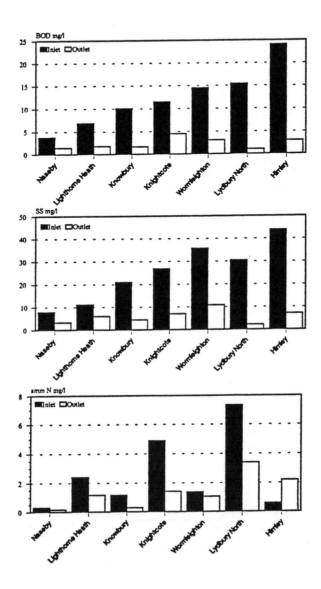

Fig. 7 Average effluent quality from sites with RBC and reed bed treatment in the period October 1992 to September 1993.

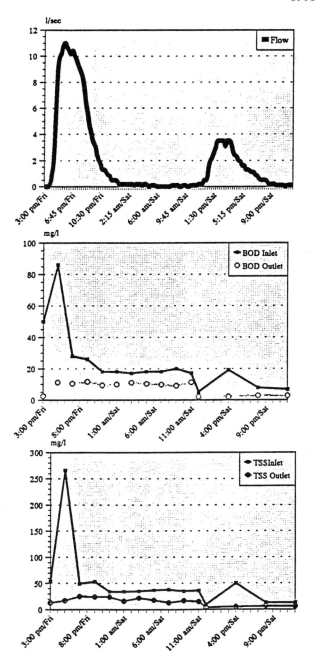

Fig. 8 Survey of the performance of storm reed beds at Lighthorne Heath (11/06/93 to 13/06/93)
(reproduced with permission of WEF, Alexandria USA ref. 6).

85

Storm reed beds

35. Whilst anecdotal evidence from plant operatives consistently endorses the benefit of storm reed beds, hard evidence is more difficult to collect. A storm hydrograph tracked at Lighthorne Heath works, is illustrated in Fig. 8.

36. The pattern of results is consistent with strongish storm sewage during first flush being diluted at higher flows by rainfall. The storm reed bed effectively buffered the peak and achieved good overall reductions in both BOD and SS.

CONCLUSIONS

37. Small works need to be designed with a robust and process flow sheet, that can ensure compliance with the appropriate discharge consent.

38. Severn Trent has adopted a process selection matrix to in order to simplify scheme management and for small works (<2000 pe) this is defined as an RBC unit and reed bed system.

39. The operating costs of RBC units are considered to be in order of 30% lower than the traditional bacteria bed and associated structures used for treatment at small works.

40. The addition of effluent polishing reed beds to the process flow sheet enables secure compliance with tighter consent standards for BOD and SS with competitive cost advantage.

41. Reed beds are emerging as an effective method of treating storm sewage overflows within the curtilage of sewage treatment works.

REFERENCES
1. CRABTREE, H. E. and ROWELL M. R.   Standardization small wastewater treatment plant for rapid design and implementation. *Proc. 2nd International conference on the design and operation of small wastewater treatment plants*, 28-30 June, 1993 Tronheim, Norway p 43.
2. UPTON, J. and GRIFFIN, P.   Reed bed treatment for sewer dykes. *Constructed wetlands in water pollution control.* eds Cooper, P.F. and Findlater, B. C.   Pergamon Press, Oxford 1990 p. 391.
3. GREEN, M. B. and UPTON, J.   Reed bed treatment for small communities; UK experience. *Constructed wetlands for water quality improvement* ed. Moshiri, G. A. Lewis Publishers, Ann Arbor 1993 p. 517.
4. FINDLAY, G. E. and BANNISTER, R. H.   Designing for reliability. Quality requirements of rotating biological contactors and reed beds. Paper presented to meeting of ICE Coventry, October 1993 *in press.*
5. FINDLAY, G. E.   The selection and design of rotating biological contactors and reed beds for small sewage treatment plants,   *in press.*
6. GREEN, M. B.   Growing confidence in the use of constructed reed beds for polishing wastewater effluents. *Proc. Water Environ. Fed. 66th Annual Conference & Exposition* **9** *General Topics* 1993, p.86.

7. GREEN, M. B. and UPTON, J. E.   Constructed reed beds: a cost effective way to polish wastewater effluents for small communities. *Proc. Water Environ. Fed. 65th Annual Conference & Exposition* **9** *General Topics* 1992 p.13.

ACKNOWLEDGEMENTS

42. The authors wish to thank the Directors of S.T.W. Ltd. for permission to publish this paper; and they are grateful for help from many colleagues in particular to M. Nunn, and S. Clay for compiling cost data.

43. Whilst reflecting the broad policy of the company any detailed statements represent the views of the authors and not Severn Trent.

Improving wastewater treatment performance in Grampian region

J. M. T. COCKBURN, BSc, CEng, FICE, FIWEM, FIMgt, Director of Water Services, Grampian Regional Council

SYNOPSIS. This paper describes measures adopted in NorthEast Scotland -more particularly in Grampian Region - to improve waste water discharges to achieve compliance with consents in terms of the Control Of Pollution Act and to meet new obligations arising from the Urban Waste Water Treatment Directive. After initially commenting on geographical, organisational and historical aspects the paper focuses on policies and practices adopted since the late 1980s to achieve these objectives.

GEOGRAPHY, ECONOMY AND ENVIRONMENT

1. Grampian Region is located in North-East Scotland covering an area of 8,800 square kilometres and has a population of about 506,000. The region features a long and frequently rugged coastline some 386 kilometres in length. Interspersed along the coast are numerous small bays and some more extensive beaches, three of which are designated in terms of the EC Bathing Waters Directive. Most of the population live along the coast, there being seven coastal communities with population equivalents over 10,000 and about thirty smaller villages. The largest centre of population is, of course, Aberdeen with a population of 250,000. Inland, there are eighteen communities with population equivalents in excess of 2,000.

3. Eight significant rivers flow through the region, being important economically as some of the best salmon rivers in Scotland and equally importantly being the main sources for the abstraction of public water supplies. Unusually for Scotland, 75% of Grampian's water supply demand is satisfied by abstractions from four of its main rivers.

4. Perhaps Grampian is most well known as the focus of much of the UK's North Sea oil and gas industries. Some 70% of UK natural gas and oil is piped ashore and processed at St Fergus. However, the traditional industries of Grampian are farming and food processing, fishing and fish processing, paper making, whisky and textiles. The Region's slogan - Grampian, Scots for Quality - not only emphasises the aim of

its traditional industries but applies equally to Grampian's natural environment. The coastal waters are generally turbulent, deep and classified as being of good quality, while the three designated EC beaches regularly comply with the mandatory standard of the EC Bathing Water Directive. Ninety nine percent of the rivers are classified as good. Only the Ythan estuary north of Aberdeen and world famous for its colonies of eider ducks is eutrophic due to agricultural nitrate runoff in its heavily farmed catchment. The Regional Council's Environmental Charter and Structure Plan place considerable emphasis on protecting and improving this environment.

ARRANGEMENTS FOR PROVIDING AND REGULATING WASTE WATER SERVICES

5. Local Government in Scotland currently comprises a two tier system of Regional Councils and District Councils. Within Grampian there are five District Councils. The Regional Council is responsible, inter alia, for the provision of water and waste water services through its Water Services Department - Grampian Water Services -and strategic planning while the District Councils have responsibility, among other services, for local planning and environmental services. Grampian Water Services currently operates 176 waste water treatment plants, 89 of which provide primary treatment (settlement), 66 provide secondary treatment (biological) and 21 provide, in addition to secondary treatment, further polishing of the waste waters before discharge. In addition, there are 82 sea outfalls all but four of which discharge waste waters into the sea, untreated.

6. In so far as waste water services are concerned environmental regulation is the responsibility of the independent River Purification Boards. Most of Grampian is covered by the North East River Purification Board (NERPB), the Highland and Tay River Purification Boards encroaching on the west and south extremities respectively. Thus the "poacher and gamekeeper" roles have, for many years, been separated with attendant benefits to the environment.

7. It may be worth noting at this juncture that the Secretary of State for Scotland intends to replace the two tier system of local government with new single tier councils and to make arrangements to provide water and waste water services by way of three public sector Regional Water Authorities covering the whole of Scotland. For this purpose Grampian is expected to be merged in the North of Scotland authority with Highland, Tayside and the Islands. In a further reorganisation the River Purification Boards together with certain environmental functions of the District Councils and HMIPI will be formed into a Scottish Environmental Protection Agency.

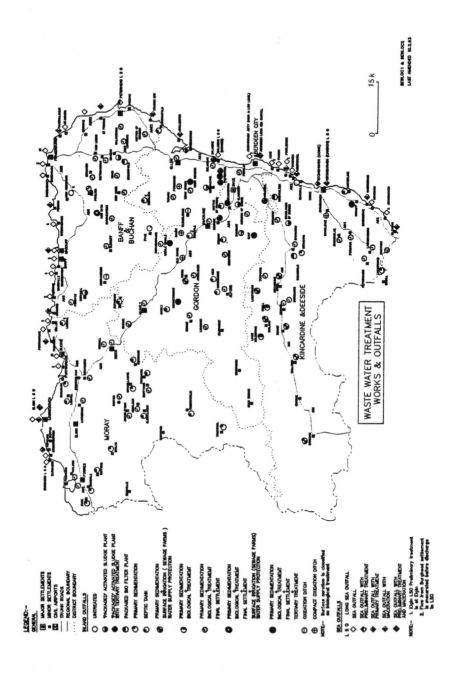

WASTE WATER TREATMENT
WORKS & OUTFALLS

15 k

SEN.OC1 & SEN.OC2
LAST AMDED 10.3.93

HISTORICAL PERSPECTIVE
8. Responsibility for the provision of waste water services transferred to the Regional Councils in 1975 when the existing two tier local government structure took effect. Prior to then, these services were the responsibility of thirty two separate councils within the area of Grampian ranging in size from large units such as Aberdeen Town Council and Aberdeen County Council serving populations of about 200,000 and 100,000 respectively to very small burgh councils serving in some cases communities of under 1,000 population. Perhaps it is not surprising, therefore, that the abilities of the different councils to provide and properly maintain waste water collection and treatment facilities varied considerably. Some of the smallest communities did not enjoy public waste water systems, some got by with increasingly inadequate systems of considerable age while, other and usually larger communities boasted relatively modern and well operated facilities. As to types of facilities commonly adopted, simple rectangular settling tanks, brick built biological trickling filters and simple sludge drying beds were popular for inland locations, while coastal communities tended to discharge to the sea without treatment and often through short outfalls that barely reached the water's edge. More unusual, at communities in the catchment of the River Dee which was the main source of drinking water for Aberdeen, waste water settlement was followed by irrigation on grass plots adjacent to the river.

9. The discovery of "Black Gold" in the North Sea in 1968 marked a significant milestone in terms of the development of North-East Scotland.

THE ARRIVAL OF THE OIL INDUSTRY AND ITS IMPACT
10. So far as waste water service provision is concerned the advent of North Sea oil gave rise to an unprecedented demand for basic onshore public health infrastructure as Grampian's population rapidly expanded and new housing and industrial development mushroomed throughout much of the area. For much of the 1970s and 1980s the greater Aberdeen commuter area had one of the highest population growth rates in UK. Aberdeen, in its leading role as the main base for the initial exploration activities and, later, the production phases, attracted the bulk of the development and thanks to the foresight of earlier City Engineers much of its underground network of sewers was of sufficient capacity to cope with the vast number of houses and industrial parks that sprang up around its periphery and discharged their waste waters into the existing system.

11. Elsewhere, small towns and villages within reasonable commuting distances of the main oil industry centres of Aberdeen and Peterhead became the focus of new development as the population expansion spread inland. For many small

communities the "bolting on" of substantial new housing, sometimes doubling the local population, gave rise to various public service difficulties, not least the adequacy of the aged waste water systems which quickly became increasingly incapable of collecting and adequately treating the much increased waste water flows of these communities.

12.   Thus, it was inevitable that Grampian Water Services, despite spending some £100 million on sewage projects generally including £40 million on major treatment or marine disposal projects between 1975 and 1988 found it almost impossible to deal adequately with the inherited problem of under-investment in waste water disposal facilities and the oil related explosion of new housing and industry. Fortunately, the nature of Grampian's rivers and coastal waters allowed its surface waters, generally, to cope with the poorer quality discharges that sometimes resulted without suffering irrevocable damage.

13.   Of the many major projects successfully completed in this thirteen year period some were of particular note. The 'flagship' project was, undoubtedly, the Aberdeen long sea outfall and preliminary treatment works completed in 1988 at a cost of £24 million but a further six major sea outfall schemes were also completed including the replacement of an earlier long outfall at Peterhead which had broken due to design and construction defects. At the same time, twenty nine projects provided either first time or upgraded waste water treatment facilities at inland locations, and somewhat unusual was the adoption of a Wimpy Unox oxygen based activated sludge process to upgrade the Persley works serving the northern part of Aberdeen.

14.   The headlong dash to accommodate the economic boom and the seemingly endless and veracious demand for housing lasted until 1986 when, overnight, the oil price collapsed. Site servicing demand ceased almost as quickly and for nearly two years stagnated. But in recent years the pace has again quickened albeit not to the hectic times of the early 1980s. Currently some £5,000,000 gross is devoted annually by Grampian Water Services for servicing housing and industry.

COPA IMPROVEMENT PROGRAMME
15. The 1986 to 1988 respite from the hectic pace of putting down new infrastructure experienced during the previous sixteen years enabled Grampian Water Services to take stock of its policies, practices and priorities in regard to waste water treatment and disposal. This was a timely review coinciding with the development by Grampian Regional Council of its Environmental Charter which emphasised the Council's commitment to protect and improve its natural environment by, inter alia, ceasing the discharge of untreated effluent to the marine environment by 2010 and, generally, improving

compliance with effluent discharge quality standards so as not to precipitate any undesirable deterioration of the Region's aquatic environment. The Council's commitment to these policies was underlined by it becoming a founder member of KIMO, an environmental pressure group of local authorities adjoining the North Sea and whose economies relied in large measure on the well being of that sea.

16. Concurrently, but independently, the North East River Purification Board reviewed its compliance enforcement policy, declaring that discharges to the aquatic environment must comply 100% with consent standards and this had the effect of putting further pressure on the Council to improve its overall waste water treatment performance. Furthermore, NERPB identified and prioritised those discharges, private and public, causing the most serious occurrences of pollution in its area, attaching to each, according to the seriousness of the pollution and the complexity of the discharge arrangements, a timescale for rectification or elimination. The Board undertook not to initiate prosecution immediately for non compliance in respect of these discharges providing Grampian Water Services undertook to progress an improvement programme within the proposed timescales. Following negotiations, a slightly modified programme with more achievable completion targets was agreed to by Grampian.

17. It may be noted that with effect from October 1993, NERPB in keeping with all of the Scottish RPAs, adopted a modified compliance enforcement policy which recognises that qualitative consent conditions in Scotland are generally strict and consequently if 75% of samples of discharges taken over a twelve month rolling period are within consent limits any exceedence is marginal then the discharge can be deemed compliant.

18. So far as Grampian Water Services was concerned these policy decisions gave rise to five important initiatives.

19. Firstly, organisational changes were made to strengthen its operational performance. On the one hand, within each divisional office, a separate works section was established to concentrate on improving the efficiency of its direct labour operational and maintenance activities while, on the other hand, each divisional operations group, which had responsibility for customer services and operational standards was strengthened by broadening senior management and ultimately by separating management responsibility for the task of treatment and disposal from the customer services/collecting systems responsibilities, so enabling each activity to be put under close scrutiny with the view to improving performance.

20. Secondly, a management review group reported on a range of initiatives which, jointly, were aimed at improving the performance of waste water treatment and disposal in the region in a cost effective manner. The group's proposals, which were implemented in large measure, ranged over the changing of working practices and priorities, the installation of low-cost but operationally beneficial technology at waste water treatment plants (eg. automatic desludging, interstage fine screening) operational manuals for each works and enhanced training of operatives.

21. Thirdly, a wide ranging operational audit of existing treatment and disposal facilities was undertaken to establish more precisely than previously the adequacy or otherwise of that which existed and particularly to identify at each locality the specific causes of deficient performance. Arising from that exercise there was developed an operational priority improvement programme. While this highlighted that in many cases real improvement could only be achieved by the application of significant capital investment, it also identified opportunities for worthwhile improvements in performance by relatively modest investment in upgrading operational plant and equipment. Typically this strategy focused on the provision of electricity to works which could then benefit from more sophisticated process plant, fine screening, auto desludging and bolt-on final polishing treatment such as pebble bed clarifiers, and sand filters. Proprietary systems such as hodwax, drum filters and Copa-products were also piloted some of which are now utilised routinely. Being essentially operational, these improvements were funded from the revenue account with up to £200,000 being so directed annually. This is ongoing.

22. Fourthly, at each community where the performance of the waste water treatment plant was substantially below the standard required by NERPB and sufficient improvement could not be achieved in a reasonable timescale usually by operational means, a partial or full embargo on further connections to the public waste water system was implemented, notwithstanding the obvious political wish not to stifle development in the region. The alternative, of course, was to accept increasing overloading of the systems with the attendant risk of prosecution for worsening non compliance by NERPB. In total, thirty three locations were targeted by this policy which remains in place being modified only as capital investment remedies deficient performance.

23. Fifthly, and arising from the foregoing a series of tripartite meetings was initiated involving Grampian Water Services, NERPB and the District Councils as planning authorities to review the overall picture of non-complying

discharges, the resulting inabilities of waste water systems to cope with further development and the need to rectify within agreed timescales the most offensive pollution occurrences. This resulted in a ten year programme of improvements being drawn up to encompass all of the perceived waste water investment needs to timescales accepted in general by all parties.

24. Whereas in 1988 the Region's waste water treatment plants registered a disappointing 56% compliance with discharge standards, by 1992 that figure had improved to 79%. While the capital investment programme played its part in bringing about that improvement it's impact was necessarily longer term. Hence it can be fairly claimed that much of the improved performance was achieved by better operational plant, more effective working practices and more focused management.

25. The capital investment programme to deal with the improvement action plan comprised a mixture of projects to upgrade and/or replace inadequate inland waste water plants and to provide, usually for the first time, appropriate treatment at coastal discharges. The bulk of the expenditure was directed towards the latter.

26. So far as the inland plants are concerned, the objective, normally, is to provide process capacity to achieve the usual 20:30 BOD:SS standard but, increasingly, an ammonia standard of 10 has also to be achieved. Activated sludge plants, often of a compact type, are most commonly selected but trickling biological filters also have a role in the improvement programme. Occasionally, smaller communities are linked together so that treatment can be provided more economically "in the centre". Auto desludging and finescreening at the inlet are standard features of plant design the latter being particularly beneficial in preventing downstream blockages and by ridding the sludge of non degradable matter.

27. At the smaller coastal communities, the aim is to intercept existing short outfalls and to transfer all waste waters from the community to a single extended outfall preceded by appropriate treatment - normally fine screens of 6mm diameter or finer. Some of the existing outfalls may be upgraded and retained for stormwater overflow purposes. Here too, the opportunity may be taken to link several communities, a good example being the North Kincardine sewerage scheme whereby six separate discharges interspersed along a 16 kilometre length of coastline have been intercepted and transferred to the Aberdeen long sea outfall system. A concurrent initiative has been to enlist public

support for a "Bag It, Bin It - Please Don't Flush It" campaign to minimise the flushing of non biodegradable items down the public waste water system.

28. The waste water systems of the larger coastal communities will be similarly improved except that treatment will normally comprise primary settlement.

29. While the public are supportive of the proposed environmental improvement programme, there is, nevertheless, much sensitivity to what is proposed particularly in relation to pumping stations and treatment plants. Concerns regarding noise, odour, loss of amenity or interference with an attractive local environment have frequently conspired to frustrate the progress of otherwise beneficial projects. Lessons have been learned and much attention is now given to public communications at a very early stage of every improvement project. The aim is always to encourage the local community to develop a sense of ownership of the intended scheme.

30. The largest project in the improvement programme is the £17 million proposal to replace existing outfalls at Fraserburgh with an interceptor system leading to a new wastewater treatment plant before discharge via a long sea outfall. Preconstruction difficulties, alluded to previously, have delayed the project by a year. Similarly high profile projects at Banff (£1.1 million) and Abercromby Jetty in Aberdeen (£4.5 million) both intended to do away with grossly polluting discharges, while being welcomed in principle, have suffered from sustained objections to detailed proposals and unrealistic land transfer valuations.

TRADE EFFLUENT CONTROL AND SURFACE WATER POLLUTION

31. The benefits accruing from the adoption of effective trade effluent control practices have been apparent to Grampian Water Services from the early days of the Regional Council. Currently, a team of eight trade effluent inspectors led by two professional scientific officers is responsible for policing trade discharges to sewer and for monitoring the quality of those discharges which are subject to trade effluent charging using the Mogden formula approach. Only seven out of twelve sewerage authorities in Scotland presently apply trade effluent charges and of the seven that do charge, most including Grampian, have chosen to phase in the full charges over three, five or even seven years. Thus, it is only now that trade effluent dischargers in Grampian are beginning to feel the full impact of trade effluent charges but only at inland locations where waste waters are subject to treatment. Most industrial discharges with the potential to attract high trade effluent charges are

connected to coastal waste water systems without treatment and hence, for the time being, escape the worst impact of the charging regime.

32.   Fortunately, much of Grampian's industry generates discharges which are relatively free of serious persistent contamination but where such discharges do occur, the dischargers have exhibited a welcome desire to co-operate with Grampian Water Services and adequately pretreat their waste waters to acceptable standards before discharge to sewers.   Indeed, there is a growing trend towards voluntary pretreatment of effluents to minimise the impact of trade effluent charges and this development has generally been welcomed by Grampian Water Services as it has freed up treatment capacity in some waste water systems which were previously overloaded.

33.   Recently, the attentions of NERPB have increasingly focused on the adverse impact on surface water discharges of casual pollution from industrial premises.   The Board has resorted to attaching numeric consent standards for BOD (typically 5) to surface water outfalls from industrial areas and has signalled its intention to prosecute where persistent failure to achieve these demanding standards is evident. Grampian Water Services, in turn, has responded by resourcing a trade effluent inspection team charged specifically with bringing about an improvement in surface water quality.   A prioritised action plan has been drawn up with the Board's agreement incorporating target dates by which particular industrial estates will have been sufficiently cleared up to limit, if not eliminate, the incidence of chronic pollution of surface waters.   Success in this regard has been due to painstaking   investigative   work   by   the   trade   effluent inspection team coupled by firm but fair enforcement of standards and by the publication of a "Guide to the Avoidance of Casual Pollution Arising from the Drainage of Industrial Premises" now in its fourth edition. Notwithstanding the successful cleaning up of surface water discharges from industrial premises, much concern remains that the Board's expectation of such discharges comprising only uncontaminated surface water can be consistently achieved bearing in mind the widely adopted practice of taking roadwater drainage into surface water systems.

URBAN WASTE WATER TREATMENT DIRECTIVE (UWWTD)
34.   The Urban Waste Water Treatment Directive will have quite a significant impact in Grampian with at least £250million requiring to be spent by 2006.   This equates to about £50 per head of the Region's population annually over the   period.   Compared   with   an   anticipated   Scottish implementation cost of around £1.7 billion Grampian's figure

represents about 15% for a region whose population is about 10% of the Scottish total. This relatively high amount is due, primarily, to Grampian's long coastline along which, as has already been mentioned, are located seven communities with population equivalents above 10,000 as well as some 30 smaller communities. The provision of the prescribed levels of treatment at each of these locations will, in turn, increase the production of sewage sludge in Grampian six fold and its disposal, by recycling to agricultural land, is a major challenge to Grampian Water Services.

35. So far as charges are concerned, the directive is likely to at least double the cost to customers by the time it is fully implemented and in the case of domestic customers this significant increase may be exacerbated by the proposed creation in 1996 of three public water authorities in place of that which presently exists, when sewerage charges for domestic customers will be separately identifiable outwith the council tax. Thus the benefit of revenue grant will be lost and with a smaller customer base, charge increases over and above those caused by UWWTD are inevitable. Of more concern, however, is the impact of trade effluent charges on certain sectors of Grampian's industrial base - notably fish and meat processing - particularly where such businesses are located at coastal sites. Not only will they incur very sharply higher charges reflecting, for the first time, the provision of waste water treatment, but this impact will be accentuated by the ending of the phasing-in arrangements which currently apply in Grampian such that, for 1993/94, reception costs only are reflected in trade effluent charges.

36. Notwithstanding these concerns, the directive has been largely welcomed in Grampian as providing a supportive formal legal framework for its environmental charter aspirations which encompass treating all marine discharges, recycling sludge for beneficial use and supporting "the polluter pays" principle.

37. Turning to the directive in a little more detail, it may be noted that, for Grampian, implementation will require the provision of:

(i)	Collecting systems	-	None
(ii)	Coastal primary treatment	-	7
(iii)	Coastal secondary treatment	-	1
(iv)	Coastal appropriate treatment	-	30

(v)	Inland treatment upgrades	-	None
(vi)	Storm overflow upgrades	-	5
(vii)	Major sludge treatment centres	-	7

38. It is important to stress that, in arriving at the above programme of improvements, the undernoted assumptions have been made:

(i)   Coastal receiving waters are confirmed as being areas of high natural dispersion following the completion of comprehensive studies.

(ii)   Aberdeen, due to its population equivalent being above 150,000 is subject to secondary treatment although it is intended to apply for an Article 8(5) derogation to permit the provision of primary treatment only.

(iii)   The adoption of the percentage reduction approach to measure performance will be acceptable for plants providing secondary treatment to discharges to inland waters.

(iv)   Unsatisfactory storm overflows are limited, at this juncture, to those overflows identified as being currently unsatisfactory by the River Purification Boards. No account has been taken of unknown overflows.

39. With regard to sludge, Grampian, having undertaken a thorough review of its disposal strategy, has focused on recycling to agricultural land with forestry also being identified as a viable outlet. An intensive market survey of the farming community is currently underway to identify the farmers preferences regarding sludge type and it is envisaged that after digestion, sludge may be made available in liquid, cake or granular form.

40. Such is the scale of the UWWTD compliance programme in Grampian incorporating as it does the potential for major engineering works in sensitive locations not to mention the location of substantial waste water treatment plants in environmentally delicate areas that, at a very early stage in the programme development, the importance of a high profile public communications exercise was identified and subsequently executed by the production of high quality explanatory booklets and widespread public meetings promoting the theme "Cleaner Coastal Waters and the Recycling of a

Valuable Natural Resource". It is reassuring that, despite the attendant costs, a high level of public support for what is proposed has been forthcoming.

41.   The funding of the programme gives rise to some concerns.   Firstly, taking into account the full extent of water and sewerage obligations and the current public sector financial climate there is no doubt that traditional government borrowing allocations will be inadequate to finance that which is required in the timescales required. At the same time there seems to be relatively little scope for adjusting priorities and rescheduling timescales, so additional funding will have to be found.   The choice seems to lie between raising charges to directly fund capital investment (CFCR - capital from current revenue) or to take advantage of private finance and in particular BOO - Build, Own, Operate - schemes. Neither is easy to sell politically. The former because of the immediate impact on charges at a time when local authority budgets are under extreme pressure and local authority elections are looming, and the latter because, taken in the context of the forthcoming reorganisation, they are shunned by local politicians as encouraging privatisation by the back door.

42.   Secondly, the RPAs while recognising the priority that must be attached to the UWWTD capital investment programme, nevertheless, are most reluctant to entertain slippage in their agreed COPA II improvement action plans.   Thus, Grampian Water Services is caught in a difficult situation of trying to respond to two priority calls on its inadequate resources.   There is a need for the Secretary of State to issue clear guidance to the RPAs as to the national priorities bearing in mind the advice issued in England and Wales following publication of "The Quality Framework" by DoE.

43.   Before concluding this section on the UWWTD it is worth commenting on the organisational arrangements made within Grampian Water Services to progress the directive's action plan. With so many inter-related strands to what is required for compliance a senior secondment has been approved at management team level specifically to manage the overall programme and, similarly, a middle management secondment has been organised to focus on the implementation of the sludge recycling strategy within the overall directive programme. Coupled with these appointments a dedicated project management team has been established to develop, in the first instance, the necessary engineering and environmental feasibility studies for each of the major coastal projects/sludge centres and within Scientific Services a unit is being formed temporarily to handle the multi-various

effluent quality investigative programmes which will be necessary to firm up on treatment proposals across the region. Another important feature of the approach adopted in Grampian is the Corporate Project Management Group (CPMG) whereby senior Water Services managers associated with the programme meet with colleagues in Public Relations, Legal Services, Planning and Property Services to take advice in broad terms on the development of the programme. Additionally, in regard to individual projects, senior local Planning and Environmental Services officers from the appropriate District Council are co-opted onto the CPMG so that from the outset the District Council is encouraged to share in the ownership of what is proposed. This arrangement has been highly beneficial.

OVERVIEW

44. Grampian Water Services' can justly claim to have coped well with the pressures of development that have been associated with its existence since 1975 while, in co-operation with the River Purification Boards, implementing a programme of waste water treatment improvements that have protected and enhanced the quality of the region's rivers and coastal waters. It's current "Cleaner Coastal Waters" initiative to comply with the Urban Waste Water Treatment Directive is set to maintain the momentum towards its objective of appropriately treating all marine discharges of waste water by early in the twenty-first century.

Poole STW extensions — case study

P. BREWER, Wessex Water Services Ltd, J. C. MARTIN, Sir William Halcrow & Partners Ltd, and J. LAING, Degrémont UK Ltd

SYNOPSIS. This paper describes the planning required to increase the treatment capacity at Poole STW; the compact primary and secondary treatment processes selected for the new extensions; and the contractual arrangements for the implementation of the M&E and civil works. The new works will increase the treatment capacity sufficient to ensure compliance with a new 20mg/l BOD, 30mg/l SS and 5mg/l ammonia consent standard. Because of the space constraints at the site, a compact treatment process based on lamella tube separators and biological aerated filters has been selected. The M&E works are arranged under IChemE Model Form of Conditions of Contract for Process Plants, and the civil works under ICE 5th Edition conditions.

NEED FOR EXTENSIONS

1. In 1980 the South East Dorset Structure Plan was approved by the Secretary of State. This Plan envisaged considerable development growth in the conurbation areas of Poole and Bournemouth and much development subsequently took place during the 1980's.

2. Wessex Water recognised the pressure that such development would cause on the water services in South East Dorset and instigated a number of measures to provide sufficient capacity. A Strategic Study was commissioned to evaluate numerous options and to recommend a strategic route for the future.

3. The two main river catchments, the River Stour and the River Avon, are approaching their limit of capacity in accepting polluting loads. Therefore, the South East Dorset Study considered the provision of some form of sea outfall as a major component of the selected scheme.

4. The lower River Stour has a long term water quality objective of Class 1B, whilst the River Avon is Class 1A, as are the minor rivers flowing into Poole Harbour. Poole STW discharges into Holes Bay and this connects into Poole Harbour. Poole Harbour is a tidal estuary of national importance in environmental and scientific terms, but does suffer from poor flushing characteristics.

5. The South East Dorset Strategy Report of 1987, recommended that whilst a sea outfall would be needed to cater for the flows up to the fifty

year horizon under consideration, in the short term inland treatment would suffice. Extensions to the works in South East Dorset and, in particular, the major works at Poole and Bournemouth would provide for a ten-fifteen year horizon and a decision of a sea outfall could be deferred until levels of effluent standards be determined.

6. The Study and the subsequent evaluation of individual sewage works were carried out in the light of the proposed EC Urban Wastewater Treatment Directive. As the river system connected with potential recreational and bathing waters, but no definitive classification had been carried out under the Directive, then extensions were based upon effluent standards as discussed with the National River Authority. At Poole STW, these were 20 mg/l BOD; 30 mg/l SS; 5 mg/l NH_3-N on a 95 percentile basis and 40 mg/l BOD, 60 mg/l SS and 10 mg/l NH_3-N on a 100 percentile basis. Discussions also covered heavy metal limits and nutrient removal, but these are likely to be only introduced in the future when the receiving waters demand such action.

7. The sewerage catchment area for Poole STW has been modelled on WASSP by Poole Borough Council using a one in twenty year return storm. These were compared with derived Formula 'A' flows, modified by catchment planning work on fully combined and partially or fully separate sub-catchment drainage systems.

8. The extensions to Poole STW will raise the treatment capacity from a population served of 129,000 to 151,000. Dry weather flow (DWF) will be 46,700 m^3/d, and flow for full treatment will be 107,700 m^3/d. As full treatment capacity was previously restricted, this represents an increase of 48% in hydraulic capacity, together with an improved effluent standard including full nitrification.

9. Historically, the sewage treatment facilities at Poole have developed, over a large site outside of the town, as two independent activated sludge plant works receiving flows either from the town centre or from the western residential areas. The eastern works serving the town centre will be downrated to produce a nitrified effluent.

10. Industrial, commercial and residential development has been allowed to encroach around the Works over the last twenty years, so that now the Works is no longer remote. This places much pressure on Wessex Water to provide an environmentally acceptable plant. Initial appraisal work considered relocation of the works, but this was not economically viable.

11. Hence, much effort has been placed into visual, noise and odour controls, and these have been the main factors in process selection. The primary objectives are to limit all odours at the site boundaries to be virtually undetectable; limit noise generation to existing levels; and to provide a pleasing landscaped, aesthetic design.

CHOICE OF TREATMENT PROCESS

12. The new treatment stream presently being constructed at the works

will cater for a DWF of 28,000 m^3/d and a peak flow of 64,000 m^3/d, giving rise to a daily BOD load of 6,973 kg and an ammonia load of 804 kg. Eventually, as the population served by the works increases towards 200,000, a duplicate second stream will be provided, allowing the existing activated sludge systems to be decommissioned.

13. Over the years, development has encroached around the works limiting the space for its expansion. As a consequence it has been necessary to select a treatment process that could be accommodated within the tight confines of the existing site. The only land available for the construction of the first phase of these new works was an area 135m by 38m, originally occupied by the sludge drying beds. A layout of the works is shown on Fig.1. Until the second stream is completed the existing treatment facilities will need to be kept operational.

14. To minimise the visual impact of the works and to ensure that no environmental nuisance will be caused to neighbours, it was decided at an early stage in the planning procedure to enclose the process and to vent all gases through odour control equipment.

15. The planning stage of the project coincided with the introduction of biological aerated filters (BAF) into the UK. The Biocarbone process had been introduced from the continent and systems such as the SAFe process were under development in this country. The compact BAF process, particularly when combined with lamella tube separators used for primary treatment, provided an answer to the space constraint problem at the Poole site. The combined process would fit within the space available, and could also be readily covered. The solution also provided Wessex with the opportunity to construct a 'show case' works for the BAF technology. Indeed, the completed works will be provided with vantage points for viewing both by operations staff and also by visitors.

16. To select a suitable lamella and BAF system, Wessex advertised for manufacturers with a proven process, demonstrated either in this country or on the continent. From the twenty or so companies who replied, a short list of three was selected to tender under IChemE Model Form of Conditions of Contract for Process Plants, the so called 'Red Book', to provide the treatment process

SAMPLING PROGRAMME

17. To provide up to date information on the nature of the sewage to be treated, a comprehensive diurnal sampling and flow measurement programme was undertaken at the works. To ensure that the tenderers were provided with the information they specifically needed to properly size their process, they were asked to identify the determinands they required to be sampled. The list included BOD (total and soluble), total solids, suspended solids, COD (total and soluble), TKN, ammonia, temperature, grease, alkalinity, pH, chlorides and sulphates.

18. The programme was carried out over a two week period with spot

samples being taken every two hours. The results of the analysis revealed that each morning a high ammonia load arrives at the works, with a peak concentration typically greater than 60 mg/l. The information was rationalised to a four hour peak load of 341 kg NH_3-N and incorporated in the process design brief given to the contractors. The high ammonia peak was found to be of concern to the process suppliers because of the need to achieve compliance with the strict ammonia standards. The compact BAF process has a short hydraulic retention, typically less than one hour at peak flow and the risk of 'punch through' of ammonia above the consented 95 and 100 percentile values could not be overlooked.

PROCESS TREATMENT

19. The contractor selected by Wessex was Degrémont UK Ltd who were contracted to provide a combined treatment system using their Densadeg and Biofor technology. A layout of the process is shown on Fig.2.

20. In view of the stringent performance standards to be applied and the limited site area available for the process, the design for the new treatment stream is based on

(a) Primary treatment comprising high rate Degrémont Densadeg lamella units with chemical conditioning.
(b) Biological BAF treatment in two stages for carbonaceous and ammonia removal with Degrémont Biofor units.

21. This process treatment concept is well established as being performance efficient and reliable in consistently meeting the consent standards for BOD_5, suspended solids and ammonia.

22. Careful consideration of performance standards related to the flows and loads, assessed from the statistical information extracted from monitoring and sampling programmes clearly established that two-stage BAF treatment was essential.

23. The Primary Treatment stage of high rate lamella settling and clarification with partial sludge recycle and enhanced with appropriate chemical dosing achieves high performance for both BOD_5 and suspended solids removal. Sludge thickening is provided within Densadeg primary treatment thus eliminating the need for separate sludge treatment ahead of anaerobic digestion.

24. Biofor treatment washwater is returned upstream of the Densadeg primary treatment, therefore there is only one sludge extraction point from the works, where chemically conditioned thickened sludge is drawn off and transferred to storage prior to digestion.

25. An added benefit of chemical dosing will result from phosphate precipitation and removal in the excess sludge.

26. To ensure nitrification in the second stage Biofor treatment sufficient alkalinity must be maintained during periods of high ammonia

load. To achieve this condition sodium hydroxide is dosed on pH monitoring and regulation ahead of second stage Biofor treatment.

27. For both Primary and BAF Treatment, sufficient units are included such that when individual units are out of service for maintenance or wash, in the case of the Biofors, performance standards are still fully in compliance over the full range of flows and loadings.

28. Hydraulic flow through the works is by gravity except for Biofor interstage transfer, necessitated to meet specific inlet and outfall constraints.

PROCESS SIZING

29. Primary Treatment

Maximum flow to Densadeg units	- 2667m³/h plus wash
	- 2667 + 427
	- 3094m³/h
Number of Densadegs	- Three
Lamella area / Densadeg	- 67m²
Total area	- 201m²
Water depth	- 5.7m

Normal duty, three Densadegs in service
Maximum flow acceptable with two Densadegs in service

30. Ferric chloride and polymer dosing is applied to the primary treatment Densadegs.

31. BAF Treatment

Maximum flow to Biofor treatment	- 3094m³/h

Biofor Stage I

Number of Biofor cells	- Eight
Area of Biofors	- 73m²
Media depth	- 3.0m

Normal duty, eight Biofors in service
Maximum flow acceptable with seven Biofors in service
(one in wash or out for maintenance)

32. Interstage stage transfer pumping between Biofor I and Biofor II

Biofor Stage II

Number of Biofor cells	- Eighteen
Area of Biofor cells	- 73m²
Media depth	- 4.0m

Normal duty, eighteen Biofors in service
Maximum flow acceptable with one Biofor in wash sequence plus one out of service for maintenance, sixteen in service.

33. Sludge

- Nature of sludge	-	combined primary and return BAF wash sludge
- Type of sludge	-	chemical conditioned pre-thickened internally
- sludge production	-	approximately 10.5t/day dry solids
- Sludge concentration	-	6.0% dry solids
- Sludge volume	-	175m³/d
- Sludge treatment	-	Anaerobic digestion (existing on-site facility)

DESCRIPTION OF PRIMARY TREATMENT BY DENSADEG

34. The Densadeg is an external recirculation unit based on the lamella settling principle. A schematic of the process is shown on Fig.3. It is fast, compact, adaptable and unaffected by variations in raw water composition and flow rate. The process also reduces the volume of settled sludge, which is then transferred for anaerobic digestion. Immediately ahead of the Densadeg ferric chloride is dosed into separate flash mixing chambers to pre-condition the raw water flow.

35. The Densadeg has two adjoining concrete tank compartments which comprise the unit structure.

(a) Flocculation chamber
(b) Settling chamber

36. The flocculation chamber is a reactor in which the polymer is introduced and mixed. A turbine mixer is provided driven from a walkway at the top of the concrete chamber. The mixer operates in a cylindrical baffle, thus pumping the raw water upwards vertically. To avoid a vortex, four plate baffles fitted to the top of the cylinder ensure vertical flow conditions. Just below the turbine mixer and fixed with a cylindrical baffle, a ring pipe injects polymer through 5.0mm diameter holes. The raw water inlet pipe is positioned vertically at the bottom of the chamber with a baffle over the inlet pipe discharge to improve mixing.

37. From the bottom of the flocculation chamber, the flow rises through a large port vertically through a transfer chamber section and over a submerged weir and then downwards into the settling chamber. In this chamber, the flocculated solids descend to become dense sludge at the bottom after continuous slow thickening with a picket fence scraper mechanism.

38. The thickened sludge is then scraped to the central sludge hopper and drawn off directly by means of a positive displacement sludge pump. A portion of the more dilute top sludge layer is returned continuously from underneath the scraper bottom by means of a separate positive displacement pump to the flocculation chamber inlet pipe.

39. The final clarification is carried out by the lamella tubular section packing with the top of the lamella approximately 500mm below top water level.

40. To regulate the sludge extraction, two level probes are fitted in the settling chamber.

41. Located after the transfer section a full width surface trough collects grease and surface floating matter for removal.

BAF TREATMENT BY BIOFOR

42. The Biofor is a biological aerated filter containing a fixed, submerged, granular bed with both the process air and effluent operating in the upflow (cocurrent) mode. A schematic of the process is shown on Fig.4.

43. The process allows two simultaneous purification functions:

(a) Biological elimination of soluble organic pollution by activated fixed biomass.
(b) Retention of suspended solids and insoluble organic pollution by filtration.

44. Previously settled raw water is distributed from an inlet feed channel into the filter at the bottom and equally distributed through nozzles on a concrete floor. The raw water rises through the media above the concrete support floor and just above the floor level process air is distributed through special Oxazur non-clog membrane air nozzles over the total filter area.

45. The raw water and process air rise co-currently through the media and the filtered aerated water passes through a special labyrinth gate and over a weir into a channel outlet. The Oxazur air nozzles are fitted to PVC pipes and connected to an inlet manifold supplying process air to the Biofor cell.

46. The organic matter which is retained within the full media volume is removed before the media bed becomes completely clogged and therefore washing of the media is necessary every one or two days, or every third day in the case of second stage Biofors.

47. A discrete washing cycle will ensure adequate cleaning of the Biofor filter cells operating either on a timer system or on head loss across the filter. The wash cycle will include both wash/air and wash only phases on a timed sequence developed to optimise actual wash requirements during commissioning.

48. The wash water supply is provided from a holding tank suitably sized for wash requirements and fed from the treated effluent supply prior to discharge to outfall. The wash water return is collected in a holding tank for return upstream of the Densadeg primary treatment for consolidation with the main sewage inflow.

49. Biofor cells are built in concrete in a modular form of construction with Stage I Biofor (eight cells) in a single lane of cells and Stage II Biofors (eighteen cells) in a double lane of cells, this layout thus forming a very compact plant 'footprint'.

CONSTRUCTION

50. The civil, architectural and structural design commenced shortly after Degrémont had finalised their process design.

51. The contract drawings were produced using computer aided draughting (CAD). This proved to be beneficial, allowing any changes resulting from modifications to the M&E works to be readily incorporated into the civil design.

52. A separate contract was let for the civil and building works under the ICE 5th Edition conditions. Work started on site in August 1992 and is due for completion in 1995.

53. To limit the height of the new inlet works in line with Planning requirements, the process sub-structure is founded, at its lowest point, 7m below ground level. It is being constructed in Creekmoor clay which overlies an artesian layer some 20m below ground. To prevent uplift of the clay during construction extensive dewatering is required to reduce the artesian water pressure. It originally stood about 2m above ground level in piezometers sunk at the site. It has now been lowered by some 7m.

54. All pipework within the structure is being provided under the 'Red Book' contract, for installation by the civil contractor. This has required close working procedures to be developed between the two contractors. To allow Degrémont early access to parts of the Works, to enable them to commence installing their M&E equipment, the works is being constructed with staged completion.

55. To minimise the environmental impact of the works the process units will be enclosed. The Densadegs, the odour control equipment, chemical storage and the dirty backwash tank, will be housed in the 'Primary Treatment' building. A matching 'Control' building will be provided to house the control room, interstage pumping station and the final effluent tank. The Biofor cells will be covered with GRP or aluminium covers. The buildings will have external tubular steel frames, detailed to conform to a Wessex corporate style. All enclosed process areas will be vented to the odour control facilities. Odour control will be achieved by chemical scrubbing.

COMMISSIONING

56.   Once the works is completed and set to work, an extensive commissioning period will begin. This will last for twelve months. From the beginning the new stream will receive its design flow from the new inlet works, being constructed under a separate contract on the site. Part of the commissioning will include intensive testing of the final effluent over two, fourteen day periods, one in winter and one in summer. Each day six, four hour composite, flow proportioned samples will be taken. The plant will be deemed to have passed if the number of test results outside the BOD, suspended solids and ammonia limits for the 95 percentile standards do not exceed the maximum number of consent failures allowed in the 'look up' table, presented in Appendix A. To check that the quality of the sewage arriving at the works is within preset limits, twenty four hour composite samples of the incoming effluent will also be taken and tested for BOD, SS and ammonia.

57.   The tests will only be valid when for BOD and SS the temperature of the sewage is above 7°C and for NH_3-N, when it is above 10°C.

58.   Weekly spot samples over the full 52 weeks will also be taken. These results too will be checked against the 'look up' table.

APPENDIX A
LOOK-UP TABLE FOR BOD, SS AND AMMONIA TESTING

Number of Samples Taken During Test Period(*) and Maximum Permitted Number of Samples Failing to Meet Standard(**)

004 - 007 (*)	1 (**)	156 - 171	13
008 - 016	2	172 - 187	14
017 - 028	3	188 - 203	15
029 - 040	4	204 - 219	16
041 - 053	5	220 - 235	17
054 - 067	6	236 - 251	18
068 - 081	7	252 - 268	19
082 - 095	8	269 - 284	20
096 - 110	9	285 - 300	21
111 - 125	10	301 - 317	22
126 - 140	11	318 - 334	23
141 - 155	12	335 - 350	24
		351 - 365	25

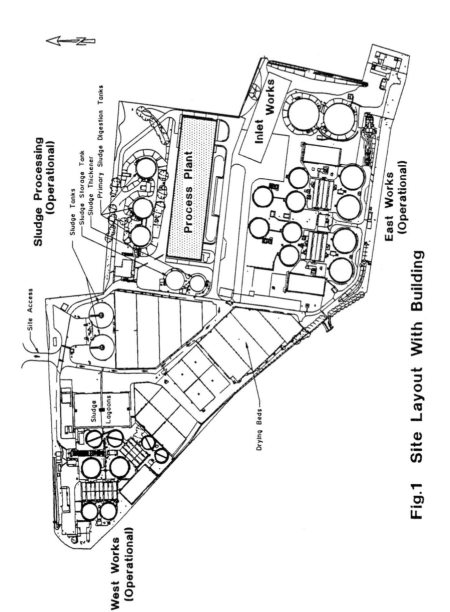

Fig.1 Site Layout With Building

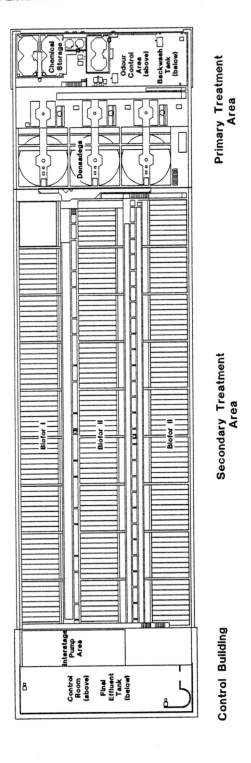

Fig.2   Process Plant Layout

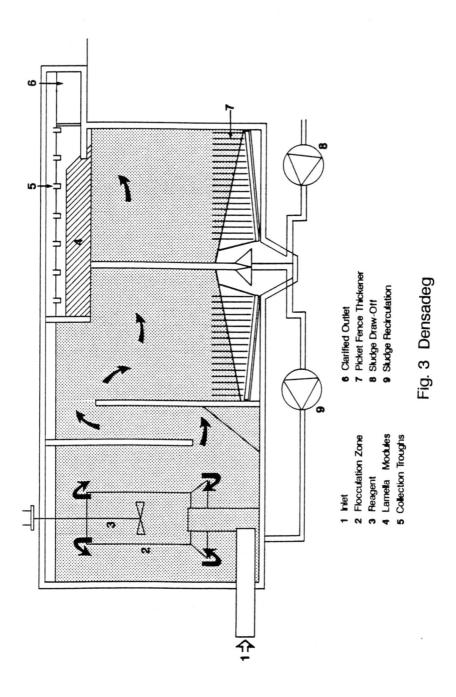

1 Inlet
2 Flocculation Zone
3 Reagent
4 Lamella Modules
5 Collection Troughs

6 Clarified Outlet
7 Picket Fence Thickener
8 Sludge Draw-Off
9 Sludge Recirculation

Fig. 3 Densadeg

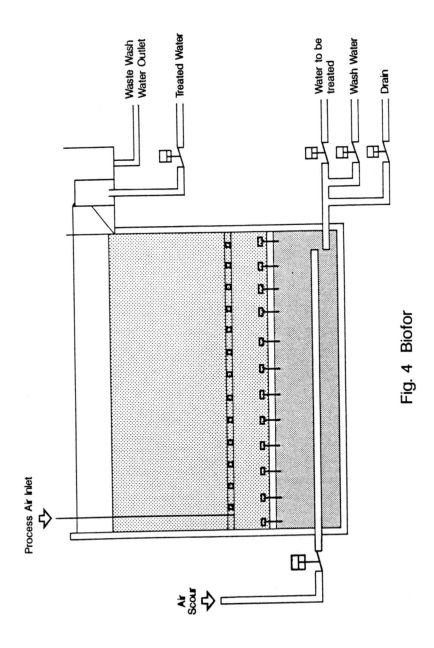

Fig. 4 Biofor

Withernsea sewage disposal scheme

P. LANGLEY, BSc, MSc, MIWEM, Sewage Treatment Technical Manager, Yorkshire Water Services Ltd, and I. AIKMAN, BSc, MSc, MICE, MIWEM, Technical Director, Babtie Group Ltd

SYNOPSIS.   During the 1980's the bathing waters at Withernsea did not consistently meet the EC standards on water quality. The wastewater disposal facilities were also unsatisfactory due to problems relating to storm overflows and associated flooding of a public recreation area. A new sea outfall, operating in conjunction with a 5500m³ detention tank was designed for disposal of both dry weather and storm flows. The £8 million scheme which includes a new treatment works, pump station and rising main was commissioned in 1993.

INTRODUCTION
Withernsea pre-1989

1. Withernsea is situated on the east coast of Yorkshire some 44 km south of Bridlington and 20 km north of Spurn Point as shown in Fig. 1.   The resident population in winter is 6,000 but this increases to 10,000 in summer through tourism. There are no significant industrial effluents.

2. The sewerage system is mostly combined and, with the exception of a minor inland storm overflow associated with new development, the whole system drains to a single point at Valley Gardens on the sea front.

3. A pump station at Valley Gardens, constructed in 1962 and still containing much of the original equipment, pumped design flows of 110 l/s through a 3 km rising main to a primary treatment works to the south of the town (see Fig. 1.). Following primary treatment, flows were discharged through a 450mm diameter outfall to a point near the low water mark some 160m from the cliff face. Storm flows were discharged from the Valley Gardens pump station to the low water mark on the main beach adjacent to the town.

4. The storm overflow pipe, also constructed in 1962, was in poor condition being full of holes due to wave action despite repeated attempts at patching (see Fig. 2).   It was also prone to blockage with beach material resulting in occasional flooding of the Valley Gardens, consequential unfavourable press coverage and concern expressed by councillors. Storm flows were unscreened.

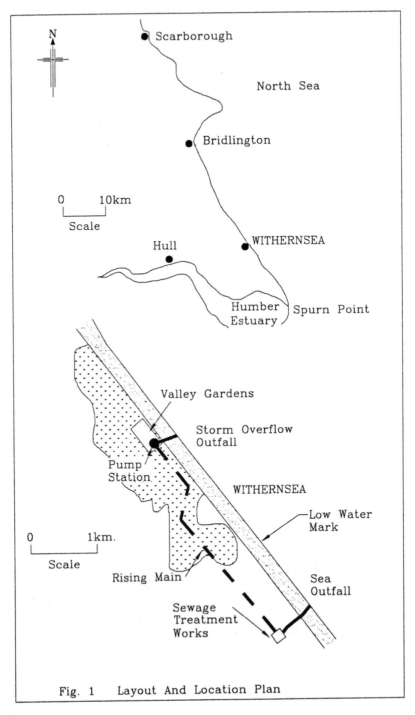

Fig. 1   Layout And Location Plan

Fig. 2 Leakage from perforated stormwater outfall

5. The rising main to the treatment works had failed on two occasions and inspection of a series of samples revealed at least half the length of main to be in poor condition and prone to further failure. In addition, its precise route through the town was uncertain and tracing revealed it to run under the foundations of at least two properties.

6. The treatment works consisted of a balancing tank, two primary settling tanks and sludge drying beds converted to use as liquid sludge storage. There was no screening or grit removal resulting in a considerable rag problem in the sludge and some visible material being discharged from the outfall whose condition was similar to that of the storm overflow pipe.

7. Flows from the outfall were taken by tidal currents back to the main EC designated bathing beach onto which storm flows were also discharged. This resulted in aesthetic problems due to the unscreened discharges, and a high median bacterial count in the bathing waters which failed the EC Mandatory standards in 1986, 1987 and 1990.

Legislation and Guidelines : The Moving Goal Posts

8. At the time the scheme was first developed, the major legal consideration was the Bathing Water Directive (ref. 1). During scheme design, however, the interpretation of the Urban Wastewater Treatment Directive (ref. 2) and the requirements of the National Rivers Authority (NRA) and Her Majesty's

Inspectorate of Pollution (HMIP) in terms of stormwater discharge became clearer.

9. The stormwater discharge was initially a conventional formula A overflow which would have required screening, During scheme development however, HMIP announced new proposals to prevent storm discharges to bathing beaches for events with return periods of less than 1 in 5 years (ref. 3). Following negotiations with HMIP it was agreed to accept containment of a 1 in 2 year storm which reduced the works required and the final scheme cost.

10. The Urban Waste Water Treatment Directive requires only primary treatment at Withernsea and, as this was already available for the original design flow to full treatment, little additional work was required. There was however a requirement by the NRA to stop the discharge of screenings which contained list 1 substances, ie plastics, hence the legislative need to provide adequate screening.

Development of the Scheme

11. In March 1987, Babtie Group were appointed to carry out a desk study to optimise the location of a replacement sea outfall and associated headworks; no other works being envisaged as necessary at that time. A marine survey, initiated in parallel with the study, covered two potential sites: one in the area of the existing outfall and one to the east of the town centre.

12. For economic and aesthetic reasons it was decided that the new outfall would be constructed from the existing treatment works site and other parts of the scheme would be renovated as necessary.

13. However, it soon became evident that provision of an effective stormwater outfall would be very costly and temporary detention of storm flows at Withernsea, followed by discharge via the proposed long sea outfall, could be a more attractive solution. This in turn led to investigation and ultimately, replacement of the existing rising main. The change in approach to disposal of stormwater coincided with similar lines of thinking within HMIP and the newly formed NRA, whose approval was required for the scheme to proceed.

14. The impact of these changes is well illustrated by the programme of work in Fig. 3 which identifies the various surveys and investigations carried out. The finally agreed disposal scheme, as illustrated in Fig. 4, was officially opened on 20 August 1993.

CONCEPT DEVELOPMENT
Physical Considerations

15. Much of the coastline between Withernsea and Spurn Head to the south comprises gently undulating boulder clay cliffs which are subject to rapid erosion by the sea. In the vicinity of the treatment works, 5m high cliffs have been retreating at around two metres per year since Roman times, due to their exposed position and the strong marine currents. The resulting characteristics of the area played a determining part in the final scheme design, i.e.,

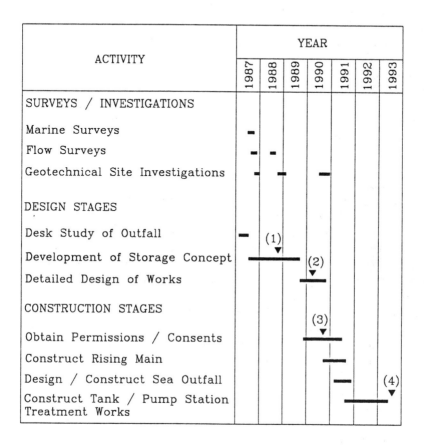

Fig. 3   Programme Of Work

NOTES

(1) HMIP issued guidelines relating to frequency of
     overflow to the marine environment.
(2) HM Government's interpretation of EEC Directive
     made public.
(3) NRA granted discharge consent for emergency
     overflow and sea outfall.
(4) Official opening of Withernsea scheme.

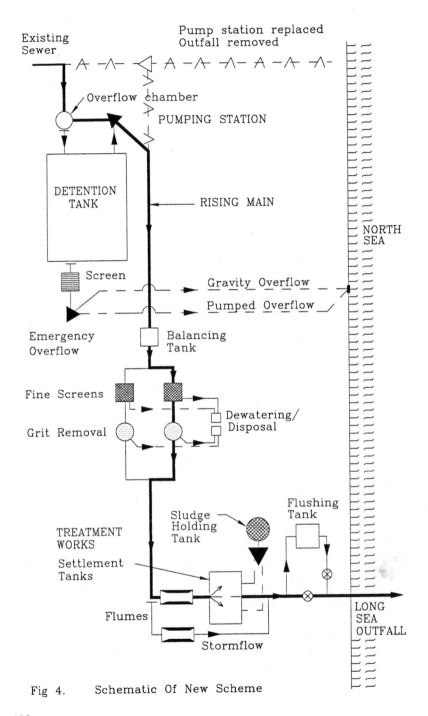

Fig 4.   Schematic Of New Scheme

(a)   boulder clay soils with random lenses of sand, cobbles and boulders

(b)   very coarse beach material, which was the cause of abrasion damage to the previous outfalls

(c)   beach levels varying by up to 4m in a single storm

(d)   frequently very turbid waters around low tide level

(e)   shifting sea bed sand dunes, particularly in the vicinity of Withernsea town.

16. The ground falls to the west at Withernsea draining to a single minor watercourse which eventually discharges in the Humber Estuary.

Control of Stormwater

17. A flow survey was carried out and a (WASSP) computer model of the sewerage system was built, verified and used to determine global run off characteristics. A simplified model was then used to optimise the proposed tank storage volume for a range of storms and tank emptying rates. The design storage volume of 4000m³ was based two stage pumping with the tank being emptied at a nominal rate of 120 l/s for stored volumes below 2000m³ and 160 l/s where the volume of stormwater in the tank exceeded this value. The normal dry weather flow pumping rate is 80 l/s.

18. For reasons of both cost and security, in the event of a power failure, a gravity fed tank solution was adopted and further 1500m³ of storage provided to deal with extreme storm conditions when a high level emergency overflow would come into operation.

19. Due to the problem of fluctuating and potentially high beach levels, the emergency overflow comprised both gravity and pumped systems, with the latter arranged in such a way that pump flows would, if necessary, clear sand away from the gravity outlet.

20. The agreed scheme involved provision of a new pumping station and storm overflow chamber in addition to the 5500m³ detention tank. For aesthetic reasons it was decided to construct the tank below an unsurfaced car park adjacent to the existing pump station, which would be abandoned, and build a new pump station superstructure.

Knock-On Effects : The Rising Main

21. The proposed increase in pumping rates resulting from detention of storm flows led to detailed check on the condition of the existing 375mm diameter rising main. The spun iron pipework was excavated at a number of points, shotblasted and subject to ultrasonic thickness measurement and laboratory testing of pipe samples.

22. Significant external corrosion was found, seriously weakening the pipeline, a factor emphasised by a burst which occurred under a house garden immediately prior to the investigations. Based on the route of the existing main, which was in part close to or under domestic properties, and its structural

121

and hydraulic limitations, a decision was taken to replace the full 3 km length.

23. The storage of stormwater and increased pumping rates also had a significant impact on the design of the treatment works and outfall.

Long Sea Outfall

24. A dry weather flow survey was carried out during the summer of 1987 to obtain outfall design data. To overcome the inherent problem of measuring low in sewer depths and velocities, a depth only monitor was installed in the pump station sump at the tail of the system. Total and base sewer flows were compared with water supply figures to separate out infiltration and assess the holiday peaks which were found to be predominantly a weekend phenomenon.

25. Based on the above data, projected water demands and population growth, the future dry weather flow and design flow rates were estimated along with the diurnal flow pattern. An outfall discharge point some 850m offshore was then determined on the basis of a 1 in 50 dilution rate (ref. 4) and a single 4 port riser, the latter being selected to minimise problems of sea water and/or suspended sediment intrusion to the outfall.

26. A computer based dispersion model of the marine environment was calibrated from previously collected field data and used in conjunction with design flows, to assess the proposed outfall discharge location with regard to the EEC bacterial standards (ref. 1).

27. Modelling the design dry weather flow situation was carried out using the bacterial concentration determined by Babtie Group from a previous analysis for the Scarborough sea outfall. For the purpose of storm flow modelling, bacterial concentrations in the marine discharge were estimated for the complete cycle of filling and emptying the detention tank, taking account of dilution by stormwater and growth and die off rates within the tank (ref. 5). Wind direction and strength for both analyses was based on long term records.

28. A significantly larger dilution plume, containing elevated bacterial levels, was predicted for storm flows than for dry weather flows, partly as a result of bacterial growth within the tank. However the proposed discharge point was assessed to meet EEC Mandatory Standards under all flow conditions and the location confirmed.

29. Hydraulic design of the outfall pipeline was based on a range of criteria including the following:-

    (a)   Flow velocity under storm flow conditions to equal or exceed the scour velocity for the maximum size of particle which would pass the screens.

    (b)   Flow velocity under dry weather flow conditions to equal or exceed the scour velocity for particles which would pass the grit removal system.

    (c)   A tank to be provided at the treatment works to allow regular flushing of the outfall.

Treatment

30. The treatment system is illustrated in Fig. 4. Pumped flow, normally some 80 l/s, enters a balancing tank which regulates the discharge to the design figure (55 l/s), and under storm conditions, allows additional flow to weir over a regulating device.

31. Flow passes through 5mm aperture screens and grit removal. A measuring flume then passes dry weather flow to settlement tanks with the balance going direct to the sea outfall. The dry weather and storm flow streams meet upstream of the flushing tank which is normally bypassed.

DESIGN AND CONSTRUCTION

Programming Pressures

32. Due to its condition, replacement of the rising main was programmed to commence as early as possible, in advance of the main civil works.

33. The high summer tourist population dictated that major works in Withernsea be executed out-of-season whenever possible. As the northern third of the 3 km. rising main is located within the Promenade, construction was commenced in October 1990, with work in the sensitive sections programmed to be completed by 29 March 1991.

34. Marine works are preferably carried out during the summer months. Construction of the long sea outfall was therefore programmed for the summer of 1991 in order to have it commissioned for the 1992 bathing season.

35. Construction of the civils works for the detention tank and pump station, which inevitably spanned the summer season, was scheduled for early completion and in fact the car park over the detention tank was back in use by the time commissioning trials were under way.

Rising Main

36. To eliminate the risk of corrosion, medium density polyethylene (MDPE) pipe was used for the replacement main in preference to a ferrous pipe. The southern section of the route along the edge of agricultural land lends itself to the laying of long lengths of butt fusion welded pipe.

37. The rising main diameter (400mm) was derived on the basis of achieving self cleansing velocities over a range of flows between 75 l/s and 160 l/s and keeping retention times in the main below 6 hours (to minimise possible septicity) whilst minimising the overall pumping head.

38. To maintain continuity of pumping between the pump station and the treatment works, the new main was temporarily connected to the existing main adjacent to the pumping station and the treatment works. The connections to the respective new structures were made on completion of the remainder of the works. This was followed by the grouting-up of the old main once commissioning tests were successfully completed.

Sea Outfall

39. As the structural design of an outfall is determined largely by laying

stresses, Yorkshire Water Services Ltd elected to use a design and construct type contract. After considering various options, the contract documents were based on the ICE Conditions of Contract (Fifth Edition), with appropriate additional clauses including specification of the hydraulic design parameters.

40. To comply with current legislation for both land based and marine sewerage related construction, over a dozen permissions and consents were required (ref. 6) with differing application times and periods of validity. Although some of the statutory permissions/approvals have to be obtained by the client, the responsibility for liaison and provision of data generally lies with the designers, who have to deal with the many statutory bodies over a relatively short period of time.

41. Due to the severe coastal erosion problem, open cut excavation was prohibited in the vicinity of the cliffs and the landward end of the outfall was set approximately 100m behind the 1990 cliff line. To deal with this, one tenderer put forward a competitive 1 km directional drilling proposal. This approach although very attractive was considered to be at risk from variable ground conditions, and the method used by the appointed contractor comprised a sloping tunnel, driven from a cliff-top segmental shaft, leading to a pre dredged trench in which the outfall was laid by the bottom pull method.

42. A survey carried out as part of the contract works revealed that severe erosion of the clay strata underlying the beach had taken place during the preceding winter which resulted in modifications to the outfall profile to maintain the specified cover/protection to the pipe for its design life.

43. The use of a construction site remote from the town had its benefits as a large area of land is required for welding and pulling the 800 m long outfall. A site immediately adjacent to the treatment works was leased by the contractor who was responsible for all claims regarding loss of use/value.

Treatment Works

44. To reduce costs and provide a flexible easily maintained system it was decided that the improvements to the treatment works would largely utilise package plant erected on a concrete base slab (see Fig. 5). The resulting works are very compact and allowed the existing system to operate unhindered during construction.

45. Design of the 27m x 18m x 400mm thick package plant base, although superficially a simple flat slab, was complicated by numerous channels, openings and ducts required to accommodate telemetry and power cables in addition to drainage and water feed pipes.

Fig. 5 Package treatment plant on base slab with flume in foreground

46. The rising main discharges into a steel balancing tank with a weir and HydroBrake controlling the flow to treatment and to the outfall. Storm flows are not subject to full treatment and in the event of power failure the whole flow can bypass the plant. The balancing tank is designed to be self-cleansing as the old tank accumulated silt and balls of fat. Five millimetre aperture drum screens are provided to meet the Discharge Consent, whilst microstrainers installed downstream of the settlement tanks supply filtered washwater to the screens, this being less costly than providing a new mains supply. Washed screenings are compacted in a press and discharged to a self draining skip for disposal off-site, as is the debris from the grit removal plant.

47. The governing level in the works is that of the weir in the primary settlement tanks which were retained to comply with the Consent criteria, introduced by the Department of the Environment during the design stage.

48. To allow the plant to be operated unmanned, automated desludging of the settlement tanks is provided and plant status signals from all key points relayed by telemetry to the regional control room.

Detention Tank and Pump Station

49. Siltation and deposition of sewage solids is a well recognised detention tank design problem which has been studied by a number of investigators. On the basis of Babtie Group's recent experience, the tank was designed as four

rectangular flat bottomed compartments (1 in 60 longitudinal fall) with a tipping bucket flushing system (see Fig. 6).

50. Unscreened flow from the stormwater overflow chamber initially fills the first compartment up to half depth, retaining the first foul flush. In the event of prolonged rain, subsequent flows spill to the remaining compartments which then all fill together. Should the design event be exceeded, the emergency overflow, protected by an 18mm manually cleaned screen, comes into operation.

51. Two dry weather flow pumps and three stormwater pumps are designed to operate in sequence to provide a continuous discharge from the dry weather flow sump and/or the detention tank to the treatment works.

52. Following emptying of tank compartments 2, 3 and 4, sluice gates allow the contents of compartment 1 to enter the other compartments and be pumped away. A 3.3m³ wave of water is then discharged from the tipping bucket down the 33m length of each compartment to remove settled silt or debris.

53. Foundation level of the 36m x 25m x 10m tank is approximately 5m below Ordnance Datum and, in recognition of the potentially high uplift pressures which could act on it, a 1m wide "heel" was incorporated round the base to increase its effective weight. For construction purposes, the contractor elected to use a steep batter for the upper part of the 12m deep excavation with conventional driven sheet piles for the lower part. The 1 in 2 slopes were protected with a waterproof membrane to prevent drying out and monitored daily to help detect any ground movement.

54. The detention tank and pump station have a comprehensive two stage ventilation and odour control system. Under normal conditions, extracted air is passed through the odour control system and discharged through a high level vent stack, masked by a brick "chimney" on the gable wall of the pump station. Under emergency conditions, high volume air flow is discharged direct through a roof vent. To provide a ventilation air intake which would not be visually intrusive, the ducts and louvres are built into a stone wall surrounding a war memorial, which had to be rebuilt to accommodate the works. The rebuilding works also allowed additional features requested by the Town Council to be incorporated.

55. Normal operation of the system is very largely automated. The status of all strategic items of equipment, including the gas detection systems, is monitored and key signal relayed to the regional control room. Thus it is usual for the system to operate unmanned.

56. As the new and existing pump stations are located close together the wholesale replacement of strategic sewers was avoided. However some rerouteing was required to divert flows to the new tank. This was largely carried out by relining, using threaded high density polyethylene pipes to reverse directions of flow, and by on-line replacement.

57. A small twin submersible pump station was constructed adjacent to the abandoned pump station to deal with flows from a low lying recreation area and adjacent public toilets. The new pump station also served to isolate the

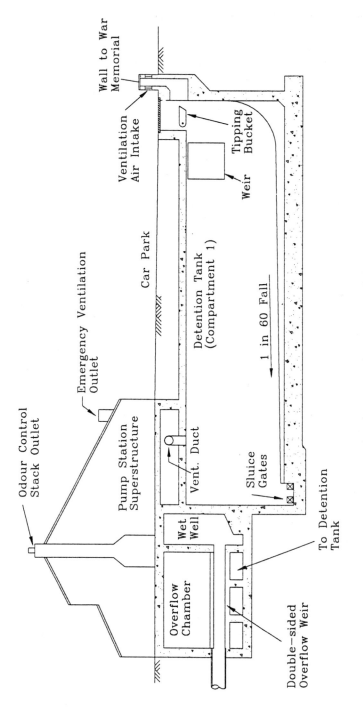

Fig. 6   Longitudinal Section Thro' Detention Tank And Pump Station

area from the main sewerage system and avoid the possibility of sewage flooding which had originally drawn attention to the inadequacies of the system and, in part, triggered the Withernsea scheme.

CONCLUSIONS

58. The Withernsea wastewater disposal scheme has eliminated the very public signs of inadequate sewerage, brought the system and bathing waters in line with current legislation, and met the requirements of the NRA and HMIP with particular regard to the frequency of overflow.

59. Attention to phasing of the works and to the interests of the local council minimised the impact of construction and maximised the visible benefits of the scheme to the people of Withernsea.

60. The detention tank, which is the core of the scheme, is designed to minimise maintenance costs, whilst automation and telemetry links built into the system ensure that operational requirements are also at a minimum.

ACKNOWLEDGMENTS

61. The authors wish to thank Yorkshire Water Services Ltd and Babtie Group Limited for permission to publish this paper. Thanks are also due to colleagues who contributed to the paper, particularly Mr P P Smith of Babtie Group.

REFERENCES

1. COUNCIL OF EUROPEAN COMMUNITIES. Directive concerning the quality of bathing waters (76/160/EEC), Official Journal of European Communities, No. L31, 1976

2. COUNCIL OF EUROPEAN COMMUNITIES. Directive concerning urban wastewater treatment (91/271/EEC), Official Journal of European Communities, No. L135/40, 1991

3. HMIP. Guidance on Long Sea Outfall - COPA Consent Application. Appendix to letter from A.S. Pearce, Head of Water Pollution Inspectorate to water authorities in England and Wales, 20 June 1988

4. NEVILLE-JONES P.J.D. and DORLING C. Outfall design guide for environmental protection. Water Research Centre Report ER209E, Swindon, 1986

5. GOULD D.J. The Effects of sewage storage on numbers of faecal bacteria and on their subsequent decay rates in marine waters. Water Research Centre Report 467-5, 1986

6. BROWN M.J. Planning and Promotion of Long Sea outfalls. Proceedings of Conference on Long Sea Outfalls, 1988. Institution of Civil Engineers, 1989, 3-16

Profitable alternatives to treatment

N. JOHNSTON, PhD, Project Leader, Centre for Exploitation of Science and Technology

SYNOPSIS. A project established to demonstrate the benefits of waste minimisation and cleaner technology has clearly shown that reductions in pollution and improvements in profitability are not mutually exclusive. In addition, the results indicate that significant savings can be achieved in the water used by industry and the effluent produced. The potential exists, therefore, to reduce or at least modify future investment in facilities for the storage and treatment of both potable water and wastewater.

WASTE MINIMISATION AND CLEANER TECHNOLOGY

History

1.   The Centre for Exploitation of Science and Technology (CEST) was established in 1987 in order to identify exploitable areas of technology and stimulate appropriate action. Registered as a charity, the centre is funded predominantly by industry with a contribution from government. Over the last seven years CEST has examined a large number of issues, markets and technologies including healthcare, materials, environment, transport and communications.

2.   Towards the end of the eighties growing concern for the environment in Europe was reflected in a considerable increase in the scope and severity of legislation to reduce pollution. CEST responded to this challenge and set out to identify the pressures for change and possible solutions. The Strategic Overview (CEST, 1991) published as a result of this work identified a number of focused projects for further study. One of these was water. Our interest in this medium stemmed in part from impending legislation but also from privatisation of the Water Utilities in England and Wales.

3.   The study concentrated on wastewater treatment, both municipal and industrial and, during the course of the study it became clear that, in response to increasing legislative pressure or rising costs, most processors (potential polluters) were considering disposal or treatment as a priority. Only a few of the larger companies were examining ways of reducing the volume, strength or toxicity of their waste.

4.   A lack of awareness combined with fear and uncertainty were the main reasons. Information on waste minimisation and its benefits was scarce and there was a fear that changes to processes would be more expensive and disruptive than treatment or end of pipe solutions. However, there appeared to be little appreciation of the risk associated with the treatment option namely that emission limits might be reduced further, making treatment more expensive and ultimately that end of pipe solutions might be unable to achieve the required level of purification. In addition, treatment requires inputs: of energy certainly, as well as management and operative time but nutrients or other chemicals may also be needed. Further, capital investment in treatment facilities can be substantial and is unlikely to show a return.

Routes to cleaner production

5.   There are, in fact, many ways of reducing pollution and Figure 1 shows the options available to processors for 'minimising environmental impact'. Those considered as 'cures' relate to the treatment of waste in its existing form whereas 'prevention' options include ways of minimising the volume or toxicity of the waste. The term cleaner technology would more accurately describe a step beyond this ie: fundamentally cleaner processes. The key point, however, is that in addition to the relatively limited range of options available as cures, consideration of waste minimisation techniques and cleaner technology broaden the range of options available to processors considerably.

Evidence of success

6.   Evidence that prevention rather than cure need not be more expensive came from The Netherlands where one of the more comprehensive investigations of cleaner technology was carried out between 1988 and 1990 under the name PRISMA (SDU, 1991).

7.   Staff and students from the University of Amsterdam and the Erasmus University of Rotterdam examined the potential for waste minimisation in ten companies covering a range of industries in the two cities. The results showed that:

    (a) over 80% of the 164 measures identified were worthy of
        consideration;
    (b) almost 50% were implemented immediately or considered feasible;
    (c) almost 70% of the measures implemented immediately had a payback
        of less than one year, 40% of them costing nothing at all.

8.   Further investigation revealed that many of the changes to processes and procedures could be considered to be simply good housekeeping. Even the technical modifications were relatively simple though one of the companies did introduce cyanide free electroplating which would have to be considered as cleaner technology.

P	**Reduction at source**
R	Product changes
E	Process changes
V	
E	**On-site recycling/re-use**
N	As raw material
T	Material recovery
I	Prevention of waste
O	Useful application
N	
C	**Off-site recycling**
U	
R	**Rendering harmless**
E	Treatment/destruction
	Storage/disposal

Fig 1. Options for minimising environmental impact

THE AIRE AND CALDER PROJECT

Origin

9.   One of the main recommendations of the CEST report "Water; resource and opportunity" (CEST, 1992) was to establish a project in the UK to demonstrate the benefits of waste minimisation and cleaner technology. Although inspired by PRISMA, the Aire and Calder Project differs in one important respect. In the Netherlands, the companies were located in two cities with little common interest other than the project itself.

10.   The project initiated by CEST is, in contrast, based on a river catchment, the Aire and Calder, which confers a number of advantages. Firstly, all the participating companies have a common interest in the health of the river since all of them discharge to the same river system either directly or, indirectly via a wastewater treatment works. Some of them also abstract water from the rivers. This focus on a tightly defined geographical area also provides a link between the participants and the community in which they operate. The range of dissemination channels is also broadened to include local ones such as Chambers of Commerce as well as the specific industry and trade associations at a national level.

11.   The Aire and Calder catchment in Yorkshire was chosen because, although the rivers rising in the west of the county are of very high quality, they flow through many industrial towns and are classified as of poor or bad quality for 25-30% of their length. The Aire, excluding its principal tributary the Calder, drains a catchment of 709 square kilometres with a population of about 1.1 million although the lower Aire carries treated sewage effluent from a population of about 1.9 million. The Calder drains a catchment of 946

square kilometres with a population of around 0.79 million.

12. it supports although there is a bias towards the manufacture of chemicals. This is reflected in the activities of the companies participating in the project.(Table 1). However, the precise activities of the speciality chemical companies are very different and there is little direct competition.

Table 1. Companies participating in the Aire and Calder Project

COMPANY	BUSINESS ACTIVITY
British Rail	Railway maintenance and engineering
Coca Cola & Schweppes Beverages Ltd	Soft drinks
Croda Colours	Dyes and pigments
Crystal Drinks	Soft drinks
DuPont Howson Printing Systems	Printing plates
Hickson and Welch	Organic chemicals
Horsell Industrial Graphics	Printing plates
Lambson Speciality Products	Speciality chemicals
Rhône Poulenc Chemicals	Speciality chemicals
Spring Grove Services	Commercial laundry
Warwick International Specialities	Speciality chemicals

13. All together, these 11 companies spend £1.7 million a year on water and £0.8 million on the treatment or disposal of liquid effluent (Table 2).

Table 2. Annual cost of water used and effluent discharged by participating companies

Water			Liquid effluent	
Metred ($m^3 \times 10^3$)	River ($m^3 \times 10^3$)	Cost (£'000)	Volume ($m^3 \times 10^3$)	Cost (£'000)
3,410	16,000	1,730	2,400	791

Structure and financing

14. Support for the project was substantial and a total of £300,000 was raised from Her Majesty's Inspectorate of Pollution and the National Rivers Authority, Yorkshire Water Services and The BOC Foundation for the Environment. A further £100,000, representing 50% of the consultancy costs, was contributed by the eleven participants.

15. A Steering Group of sponsors, chaired by CEST, oversees the project which is managed by March Consulting Group. The role of the consultants is to enable the personnel within the participating companies to undertake some of the assessments and to identify options for change so they own the

solutions and are committed to them. This also ensures that the process of minimising waste and substituting cleaner processes continues after the consultants have completed their task.

16.   The primary objective of the project is to demonstrate that a systematic approach to pollution control based on prevention rather than cure is likely to pay dividends in the long run. Attention is focused on prevention through changes to procedures and fundamentally cleaner technology. The controlled nature of the experiment will enable accurate data on costs and benefits to be collected and the project should identify gaps in the supply of products and processes as well as gaps in our knowledge which can be satisfied through development or research. A further tangible output is a manual which will enable processors who do not wish to use consultants to implement a programme using their own resources.

17.   It is important to appreciate that the primary objective of this project is *not* to improve the quality of the river which is determined by many factors outside the control of those participating. In any case it is unlikely that the actions of eleven companies will have a significant impact on the quality of the river though it is hoped that reductions in emissions will be significant.

18.   River quality is likely to improve, however, when other companies in the catchment adopt similar measures to reduce their emissions. Although the focus is on liquid effluent, it is a requirement of the project that none of the polluting load from this source be transferred to other media and many of the measures to reduce emissions do involve solid or gaseous wastes.

RESULTS

Results to date

19.   A year after the launch of the project, participating companies have implemented changes which will save them about £2.2 million a year. A similar amount could be saved if all the feasible measures were implemented. Most have identified savings worth at least £50,000 annually and one company, Coca Cola, believes it can save at least £1.6 million a year. However, although the original focus was on reductions of emissions, it is reductions in the use of inputs such as water, energy and raw materials where most of the savings have been and will be made (Table 3).

20.   Over 500 options for improving efficiency have been identified and many already implemented. In some cases, cost reduction is the main driver and in others environmental considerations come first. As expected, many of the options are extremely simple and can be implemented almost immediately. "Tens of thousands" according to one participant, "simply by the turn of a valve". Another identified a 2.5% saving in water usage on the first day. Prospects for the introduction of cleaner technology are also good and are described below.

Table 3   The impact of measures identified

	Measures		Annual Savings			
	Total		Achieved		Potential	
	No.	%	(£000)	(%)	(£000)	(%)
Inputs						
Water	140	19	186	9	473	22
Raw materials	163	22	1,310	61	788	37
Energy	93	13	112	5	356	17
Sub-total inputs	396	54	1,608	75	1,617	75
Outputs						
Liquid waste	239	32	197	9	389	18
Other	108	14	351	16	143	7
Sub-total outputs	347	46	548	25	532	25
TOTAL	743	100	2,156	100	2,149	100

21.   Only 2% of the measures identified were rejected as unfeasible and 28% were implemented immediately because they incurred little or no additional cost (Table 4).

Table 4   The feasibility of measures identified by all companies

	Imple-mented	Feas-ible	Study begun	Study not begun	Un-feasible	TOTAL
(Nos.)	150	265	45	71	11	**542**
(%)	28	49	8	13	2	**100**

22.   Just over 80% of the measures will be implemented within twelve months (Table 5) leaving just 18% to be implemented during the next year. The reason for the rapid uptake is the relatively short payback periods. Over 70% of the measures have a payback of less than one year and only 10% will take more than two years to see a return on investment (Table 6).

Table 5   Schedule for implementation of measures by all companies

	Imple-mented	0 - 6 months	7 - 12 months	>12 months	Un-feasible.	TOTAL
(No.)	150	123	162	96	11	**542**
(%)	28	22	30	18	2	**100**

Table 6   Estimated paybacks

	Cost Neutral		Estimated pay back from other measures				TOTAL
	Meas-ures	Savings (£'000)	<1 yr	<2yrs	<3yrs	> 3yrs	
(No.)	51	400	260	77	26	16	**427**
(%)	12		61	18	6	4	**100**

Implications

23.   Industry   For manufacturing industry the implication is clear. Reduction in the environmental impact of manufacturing processes need not cost money and may actually improve profitability since the greatest impact is likely to be on inputs not outputs. Thus, environmental regulation can act as a stimulus to improve process efficiency and, therefore, profitability and competitiveness.

24.   Water companies   For the water utilities, there is the possibility that investment in fresh water supplies or wastewater treatment facilities may not have to be on the scale originally planned and/or that the performance criteria of storage and treatment facilities may be different.

25.   On the evidence of the Aire and Calder Project, it appears that 10 - 14% savings in water use and effluent production are readily achievable (Tables 7 and 8). However, the potential is to reduce industry's consumption of water by at least 27% while, theoretically, effluent production could be reduced by 38%. As far as organic loading is concerned, the discharge of COD to sewer has been reduced by 284 tonnes per year through the measures already implemented with the potential for a reduction of around 5,000 tonnes.

Table 7   Summary of minimum savings in water usage;
all companies at 24th September 1993

	Volume (m^3)	%	Cost (£'000)	%
Achieved	333	10	186	11
Assessed	590	17	473	27
TOTAL	**924**	**27**	**659**	**38**
Water used (metered)	3,410	100	1,730	100

Table 8   Summary of minimum savings in effluent discharged; all
companies at 24th September 1993

	Volume (m^3)	%	Cost (£'000)	%
Achieved	333	14	197	25
Assessed	583	24	389[a]	49
TOTAL	**916**	**38**	**586**	**74**
Effluent discharged	2,400	100	791	100

a   excluding potential savings due to installation of reed beds at British Rail

26.   The eleven participating companies may not be representative of British industry as a whole so it remains to be seen how widely these results can be replicated. However, the sample does include both intensive and less intensive users of water for both process and cooling purposes and one has to consider the implication for the water utilities seriously. Although there may be a decline in income from trade effluent charges, a reduction in the volume and strength of industrial wastewater offers the water companies the opportunity to reduce or modify their plans for investment in storage and treatment facilities for both potable water and wastewater.

27.   Not all companies have a problem with water resources but virtually all have at least isolated examples of over abstraction of either surface or groundwater. A strategy to reduce demand through minimisation of water use and wastewater generation could make a significant contribution to solving these problems. There is also the opportunity to reduce the operating costs of wastewater treatment facilities through the removal of some of the more toxic substances from industrial wastewater, thereby allowing treatment facilities to run more efficiently. One way in which water companies could examine the impact of demand management on their operations is to concentrate on just one wastewater treatment works where input from industry is significant.

28.   Finally, new markets are available to the water companies for analysis of water and effluent, for consultancy and training and for some of the equipment which will be needed for the more fundamental changes to processes.

29.   The supply industry Two years ago, CEST (1992) suggested that suppliers of effluent treatment plant to manufacturing industry would have to become more broadly based. There appeared to be a need, confirmed by this study, for companies which understood manufacturing processes and which could examine the potential for waste reduction and cleaner technology before assessing treatment options. Consulting engineers and consultants are satisfying this need to some extent but it remains to be seen whether the treatment industry, including the waste management companies, have perceived the opportunity or threat which a more holistic approach may bring.

30.   Central government   It is suggested that the prime reason that industry has not been quicker to adopt cleaner production is uncertainty. Firstly, there is uncertainty over the regulatory environment, both current and future, and there is also uncertainty about the strictness with which regulations will be enforced. The role of government is to reduce this uncertainty to the point at which action is initiated. The provision of financial assistance is only one way in which this can be achieved and may not necessarily be the most important.

31.   Secondly, industry needs to be sure of what it is required to do. Standards or limits must be clearly defined and, if there is an intention to raise standards in the future, these also need to be clearly defined. Thirdly, industry should be be under no illusion that legislation will not be enforced and, that the consequences of failing to comply are not serious. Where fines are involved, these need to be reasonably consistent across the country and sufficient to stimulate action.

32.   In order to respond to these demands industry will require time to change its operations. Particularly if the intention is to encourage the adoption of cleaner technology as opposed to end of pipe solutions, at least three to five years has to be allowed for these fundamental changes and much longer periods for some industries.

33.   It is suggested that the best use of Government investment is in support for appropriate research and development, demonstration of benefits of suitable techniques, dissemination of results and the provision of information. However, since indications from both the Dutch PRISMA programme and the Aire and Calder project in the UK suggest that industry is likely to gain financially from minimising waste and the adoption of cleaner technology, assistance should be limited to examples with a high element of originality and where leverage of private investment is greatest.

34.   The adoption of cleaner production depends as much on the availability of suitable technologies and techniques as it does on appropriate financial assistance from government. There is a clear need, therefore, for governments to ensure that the technologies emerging from government sponsored research and development satisfy the needs of industry. It is suggested that this is best done by 'internalising' environmental considerations so that they become just another set of criteria for the development of process technology rather than being considered separately. This applies as much to the education and training of management and operatives, ie the software, as it does to the hardware or technology. Indeed, the Aire and Calder demonstrates that a great deal can be achieved through changes to working practices.

Technology needs

35.   Although much of the savings identified as a result of the Aire and Calder project were achieved through relatively simple changes to processes, the study has highlighted opportunities for the supply of cleaner technologies

(Table 9). At this stage it is not clear whether some of these needs could be satisfied through existing suppliers or if some development or research will be needed. However, they are likely to be common needs across industry sectors and certainly spanning much of the European Community and beyond.

Table 9   Technology needs

Cleaner Technology	surface preparation of printing plates coating of printing plates (low solvent) nitration without sulphuric acid more efficient bromination radio frequency drying dry seal vacuum pumps easy clean coatings for trains
Process control	de-aeration with nitrogen sampling of batch processes
Membrane separation of	dyestuffs, salts, solvents, organic intermediates, sulphuric acid
Analysis	Total Organic Carbon Chemical Oxygen Demand, Toxicity

Success Factors

36.   Although only half way through the study, the success of the project is already evident and can be traced to a few important factors. Firstly, the local nature of the project is a powerful motivating force. In addition, because the focus is geographic rather than an industry sector, there is less competition between the companies and they are more ready to share information and experiences. This 'club' of participating companies thus becomes very supportive of individual actions. Local media also have an important role to play in covering the project and ensuring that the local population is aware of what industry is trying to do to reduce its impact on the environment.

37.   Secondly, the arm's length relationship with the regulators is essential. There is no question of any processor being treated more leniently by the regulators simply because they are participating in the project. Indeed, some of the participants have been prosecuted during the course of the study. However, no information collected in site audits is made available to the regulators.

38.   Thirdly, the commitment of the participating companies has been high, partly because they have contributed financially to the study. Although the cost of employing consultants is subsidised, the companies are paying half the consultancy costs amounting to between £6,000 and £20,000 each. Even so, the wholehearted commitment of senior management is essential and there has to be project champion within the company to maintain momentum.

39. Fourthly, a steering group of sponsors is vital and it may be beneficial to have an independent chairman to provide a degree of impartiality, particularly if the objectives and demands of the sponsors are diverse. In situations where the regulators are not sponsors it could be an advantage to have their local representatives on the steering group.

40. At a more detailed level, it is clear that companies which follow a structured approach to waste minimisation have most to gain and that the most important elements are:

    (a) engagement of production staff in the project from the start;
    (b) accurate determination of a base line before improvements are assessed;
    (c) appropriate metering of water consumption and effluent generation;
    (d) rigourous identification , characterisation and quantification of waste streams;
    (e) adoption of formal monitoring and targeting techniques to record and quantify improvements.

41. However, the study confirmed that, provided there is commitment from senior management and sufficient human resources are allocated, valuable improvements can be made using a more informal approach. This involves simplified measurement techniques in place of more elaborate metering. Thus smaller companies should be just as capable of benefiting from waste minimisation techniques as larger processors.

42. Finally, although the intention is to train the processor's own staff to enable them to identify options for waste reduction, the consultant has to have sufficient understanding of the process to gain the confidence of the staff and to assist with the identification and assessment process.

The Future

43. As well as the Aire and Calder project in Yorkshire there is now a similar project on the Mersey, entitled Project Catalyst funded by the BOC Foundation and the Department of Trade and Industry (DTI). Initiatives are being considered in other parts of the country and individual companies are implementing waste minimisation strategies as part of their commitment to total quality management or environmental programmes. However, there remain sectors of industry where progress is still slow. In order to stimulate action in some of these sectors and to act as a national focus on waste minimisation and cleaner technology, HMIP has awarded CEST a contract to disseminate the results of the Aire and Calder and other projects more widely. In addition, CEST will provide a clearing house for the technology needs identified during the course of the projects so that British suppliers and our science and technology base have the opportunity respond to these demands.

44. Water is a finite resource in quality as well as quantity. In the longer term, it is in everyones' interest to ensure that our use of water is optimised. As effluent charges and the cost of water rises inexorably, industry will increasingly focus on improving process efficiency. The benefits of demand management for the water industry are more subtle but no less significant and it should not be long before water companies appreciate that there are indeed profitable alternatives to treatment.

REFERENCES
1. CEST.   Industry and the environment; a strategic overview. CEST, 5 Berners Road, Islington, London, N1 0PW, England, 1991.
2. CEST.   Water; resource and opportunity. CEST, 5 Berners Road, Islington, London, N1 0PW, England, 1992.
3. SDU.   The PREPARE manual. Published by the Dutch Ministry of Economic Affairs and available from SDU/DOP, Rooseveltstraat 52-56, 2321 BM Leiden, The Netherlands, 1991.

Sewage sludge incineration in Yorkshire

J. M. TAYLOR, CEng, MInstE, FIWEM, Director of Water Services,
Yorkshire Water Services Ltd, and J. V. KWIECINSKI, BSc, CEng,
MIMechE, Senior Project Manager, Babcock Water Engineering Ltd

SYNOPSIS. Yorkshire Water Services Limited
have in 1987 initiated a sewage sludge incineration
programme for the disposal of sludge arising from the
major population and industrial centres in the Yorkshire
region. Three plants have been constructed to date
and the proposals for the fourth plant are well advanced.

INTRODUCTION

1. The history of sewage sludge incineration dates back to
the 1930's, with the first plants being constructed in the
United States. The process did not become popular until
the 1960's and to date there are hundreds of plants
operating in America. Incineration is also a major sludge
disposal route in Japan and continental Europe. In the
U.K. sewage sludge incineration was pioneered in the
Yorkshire region with one of the first plants, a two stream
multi hearth incineration plant, being constructed by the
Sheffield Corporation at the Blackburn Meadows Sewage
Treatment Works. The plant was commissioned in 1968.
In 1972 and 1977 respectively sewage sludge incinerators
were also commissioned at the Knostrop Sewage Treatment
Works in Leeds and the Esholt Sewage Treatment Works in
Bradford. In the period to 1981 13 sewage sludge incineration plants were constructed in the U.K. These plants
had very limited success and most were closed down after
only a short period of operation. These "first generation"
U.K. plants were in many cases generally poorly designed
and operation was unreliable and expensive with significant
quantities of support fuel being required. The viability
of these plants was further put into question by the increase
in fuel costs following the Middle East crisis. As a result
sewage sludge incineration in the U.K. developed a reputation
of being a process with:

- a high capital cost
- a high operating cost
- suspect reliability
- adverse impact on the environment

2. For these reasons the Yorkshire plants at Esholt and Knostrop were decommissioned after only a few months of operation. Sludge disposal at these works reverted to the more traditional disposal routes of agricultural land, licensed tip and sea.

3. At Sheffield, however, the sludges were heavily contaminated by wastes from the steel industry and were not suitable for agricultural land disposal. Tipping sites are at a premium in the area and sea disposal is expensive due to the distance to the coast and the large quantity of sludge being produced, some 15,000 tonnes dry solids (TDS) per annum, from a works with a population equivalent of 625,000. The Blackburn Meadows incineration plant operated continuously until April 1990 when it was decommissioned to make way for the second of Yorkshire Water's new generation of fluidised bed sludge incineration plants.

CURRENT YORKSHIRE WATER INCINERATION PROGRAMME
4. In the mid 1980's sludge disposal problems in Yorkshire were becoming acute, especially in the heavily industrialised western part of the region. The terrain in West Yorkshire is hilly and the amount of suitable agricultural land is restricted resulting in high transport costs and dangers of pollution caused by run-off. The tipping and sea disposal routes suffered from similar problems to those in the Sheffield area.

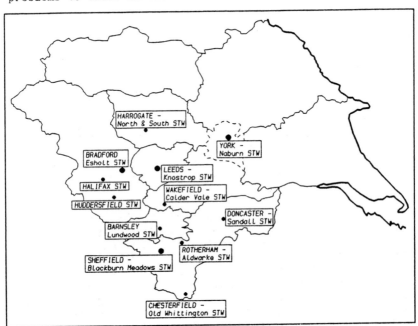

FIG 1 MAIN WORKS IN YORKSHIRE

5. In order to address these problems Yorkshire Water commissioned a sludge treatment and disposal strategy which was completed in 1986 and which considered the major sludge disposal routes of agricultural land, landfill, sea and incineration. The recommendation of the strategy report was that incineration was the most secure and economic long term sludge disposal option for sludges arising from major conurbations. Bradford, Huddersfield, Halifax, Leeds and Sheffield were identified as areas where this technology would offer the optimum solution to the sludge disposal problem. A number of plants in Europe were visited in order to gain assurance that developments in technology since the 1970's had overcome the problems that beset the earlier British installations.

PLANNING STRATEGY

6. The board of Yorkshire Water were conscious of the potential resistance from the planning authorities and general public due to the association of sewage sludge incineration with the incineration of toxic wastes. In order to overcome these fears and prejudices a planning strategy was developed designed to minimise any likely objections and which was based on the following:

- construct a full scale demonstration plant in the least sensitive area
- design the plant to meet the latest environmental standards

For these reasons Esholt Sewage Treatment Works was chosen as the location of the first plant despite the fact that the sludge disposal problems at some of the other sites were more severe. The site is located away from any residential areas and is well screened by wooded hills. As stated previously, a sludge incineration plant had been commissioned at Esholt in 1972 and the old incineration building was suitable for housing the new plant. It was anticipated that planning approval would not be required if any changes to the visual appearance of the building were minimised as the new plant would not constitute a change of purpose.

7. At the time the U.K. emission standards were embodied in BPM 11 and were considerably more lax than the latest standards which had come into force in Continental Europe. Anticipating similar improvements in British emission standards, and being mindful that Esholt was also intended to act as a reference plant to be used to appease public concern when applying for approval to construct similar plants in more sensitive areas, the board of Yorkshire Water decided that the plant should be designed to meet the then most stringent standards in the EC, the West German TA Luft 1986 emission standard.

In addition plume suppression equipment, odour control and low noise levels were also included in the specification and were designed to minimise the impact of the environment.

8.   Following discussions with the local planning and environmental health officers, approval was given for the plant without the need for a formal planning application. The Esholt incinerator has met the environmental standards set and since commissioning has been an invaluable tool in assisting the planning approval process at the other sites in Yorkshire Water's incineration programme with planning approval having been obtained for the plants at Sheffield, Huddersfield/Halifax and Leeds.   The Esholt incinerator has attracted considerable attention both in the U.K. as well as abroad and a number of other U.K. water companies have now embarked on their own sludge incineration programmes, the Esholt plant helping to demonstrate that sewage sludge incineration is one of the most environmentally acceptable means of sludge disposal from large industrialised population centres.

PLANTS CONSTRUCTED TO DATE

9.   Plants constructed and commissioned so far are given in Table 1 below:

PLANT	CAPACITY	ORDERED	COMMISSIONED
Esholt	18,000 TDS	March 1987	April 1989
Blackburn Meadows	15,000 TDS	March 1988	April 1989
Calder Valley	24,000 TDS	May 1990	Feb 1993

TABLE 1   INCINERATION PLANTS COMMISSIONED TO DATE

ESHOLT

10.   The Esholt works serves the city of Bradford with a population of 316,000.   Textiles is the principal industry and this increases the population equivalent to 900,000 with a resulting sludge production of approximately 18,000 TDS per annum.   Pre 1989 and prior to the commissioning of the incineration plant, sludges produced at the works were disposed of to agricultural land.

11.   This sludge to land operation required some 12000 vehicle movements per annum and the scarcity of suitable arable land in the immediate locality resulted in average distances travelled of some 8 miles.

12. Since April 1989 the majority of sludges produced at Esholt plus some imports from nearby works have been disposed of by incineration in the new plant.

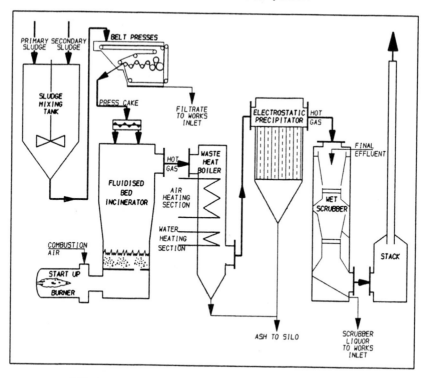

FIG 2   SCHEMATIC OF ESHOLT SLUDGE DEWATERING
AND INCINERATION PLANT

13. At the Esholt works there are some 75,000m³ of sludge storage equivalent to approximately four months of the works sludge production. Primary and secondary humus sludges are stored separately before being transferred for thickening in consolidation tanks located some 150m from the incineration plant building. As part of the scheme, sludge transfer mains were laid from the consolidation tanks to the incineration plant building. Progressive cavity pumps were installed in the consolidation tank pumping station giving the facility to vary the ratio of primary to secondary sludge being pumped to the incineration Plant. The two sludge streams are received in a blending tank and mechanically mixed prior to being transferred to the dewatering stage.

14.   The dewatering plant consists of three belt presses designed to operate as two duty and one standby. The Esholt plant requires a sludge cake of 30 to 32% dry solids for the incineration process to be autothermic and following extensive dewatering trials it was concluded that the above dry solids content could be achieved and the plant was not equipped with a thermal drier. However, due to fluctuations in sludge dewatering characteristics, to achieve the required dry solids content generally all three presses are operated together. Also advantage is taken of the large storage facilities at the works to vary the ratio of primary to secondary sludges to ensure adequate dewaterability of the resultant mixture.

15.   At the design stage there was some concern regarding the reliability of long length and lift drag link conveyors as well as the cost and reliability of solids handling pumps, and the decision was taken to locate the press hall at high level adjacent to the kiln and thus minimising the sludge cake transfer distance. This arrangement was readily accommodated within the existing building. At Esholt the length of the drag link conveyor transferring the cake from the dewatering hall to the kiln has been restricted to 17m and this item of plant has operated with very little maintenance. This has not been the case at the other two plants where the long, high lift, drag link conveyors feeding the kilns have required frequent attention. Sludge cake is fed to the kiln via two drop holes at the top of the chamber. The incinerator is of the fluidised bed type, has a bed diameter of 4.2m and contains some 12 tonnes of sand. The kiln operates under negative pressure generated by a forced draught fan feeding combustion air to the incinerator, and by an induced draught fan discharging the clean flue gases to the stack. All the products of combustion, including ash, are discharged from the top of the kiln at a temperature of 850 to 900°C to a heat recovery unit (HRU). The HRU consists of two stages, a combustion air preheat stage and a boiler stage. Combustion air is preheated to approximately 620°C prior to being fed to the kiln whilst in the boiler section water is heated to approximately 170°C for use elsewhere on the plant. A heat dump facility is also provided to discharge surplus heat to the atmosphere. The HRU was specified to cool the flue gases to 250 ± 30°C. The cooled products of combustion are then passed to single field electrostatic precipitator (ESP) where some 95% of the ash is removed and pneumatically conveyed to a silo from which it is transported by road for disposal at a licensed tip. The flue gases are then passed to a two stage scrubber and are washed with the works final effluent which has been dosed with caustic soda, thus neutralising acidic compounds.

16.   The saturated cleaned flue gases, now at some 60°C, are then passed via the induced draught fan to the base of the stack which contains a cyclone for water droplet removal. The gases are then mixed with reheat air which has been heated to approximately 150°C by means of the hot water produced in the boiler section of the HRU. The resultant mixture, now at 100°C, is discharged out of the 35m stack. Reheating the flue gases suppresses plume formation down to ambient temperatures of -5°C.

17.   Energy from the process is also used to heat the adjacent works offices. Whilst the plant has generally operated satisfactorily and economically, with operating costs being within the original budget, the plant has yet to achieve the target 8,000 hours run in any one year. Also, whilst under test conditions the plant can be operated at the guaranteed throughput of 2250 kg per hour, under normal operation, and particularly during periods of warm weather, this rate of burn is rarely achieved.

18.   One of the reasons for the difficulties in achieving the design throughput has been the lack of capacity in the heat recovery system. The flue gas exit design temperature of 250 ± 30°C has not been achievable, typically the exit temperature being in the range of 300 to 330°C. An up-grading of the system was carried out by the contractor during the annual shut-down in October 1993. An immediate reduction in the flue gas exit temperature to 220°C has been realised. Allowing for fouling during operation between the annual shut-downs it is anticipated that the maximum likely flue gas exit temperature will be in the region of 240°C. The effect of these changes on plant throughput is still to be determined.

19.   The plant has not attracted any adverse reaction from the general public. The noise attenuation measures, odour control and the suppression of the plume have minimised the risk of disturbance to the local residence and the reduction in vehicle movements from the 12,000 per annum associated with the sludge to land operation to some 700 for ash disposal and fuel and chemical deliveries means that the benefits resulting from the Esholt sewage sludge incineration plant are felt in a wide area around the plant.

BLACKBURN MEADOWS

20.   The Blackburn Meadows works serves the city of Sheffield and a population of 452,000. Steel production is the principle industry and the resultant population equiv-alent being treated at the works is 625,000. The sludge produced at the works is a cosettled primary and activated secondary sludge with considerably poorer dewatering characteristics than the sludge being treated at Esholt.

Dewatering trials indicated that a sludge cake of only 24/25% could be expected and the main differences between Blackburn Meadows and Esholt are that centrifuges were selected as the dewatering units and a thermal drier has also been provided. Also the heat transfer medium is thermal oil as opposed to the high pressure hot water system at Esholt.

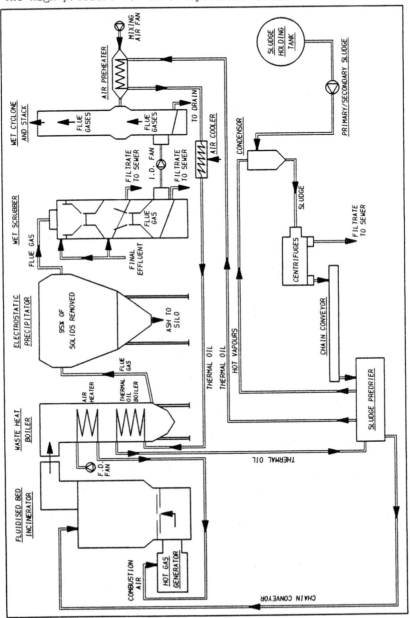

FIG 3   SCHEMATIC OF BLACKBURN MEADOWS SLUDGE DEWATERING AND INCINERATION PLANT

21. The capacity of Blackburn Meadows in tonnes dry solids terms is at 15,000 TDS less than Esholts 18,000 TDS. However, due to the lower mean ash content of the Blackburn Meadows sludge the thermal capacity of the two plants is very similar and the two kilns are of the same size.

22. Since take over the plant has operated satisfactorily. Howver, as at Esholt, the plant has yet to achieve the expected 8,000 hours operation with 7,500 hours being a more realistic norm.

CALDER VALLEY
23. The Calder Valley sludge incineration plant is a departure from the previous plants insofar that whilst the Esholt and Blackburn Meadows incinerators were constructed to dispose of sludges principally arising at those works, the Calder Valley plant serves a wider area. Normally sludges from 10 works are incinerated at the plant with a total projected 1998 sludge production of 24,000 tonnes dry solids, 80% of this sludge production arising at 3 works, Huddersfield, Halifax and North Bierley.

24. Currently the sludge arisings from the above works are in the order of 18,000 to 19,000 dry tonnes per annum, the anticipated year 1998 sludge production level only being reached following the completion of major works extensions at Huddersfield. Currently the spare capacity is being used to alleviate sludge disposal problems at other works.

25. The sizing, location and means of transportation of the sludges from the feeder works was the result of an extensive study the result of which is an incineration plant located at the Brighouse Sewage Treatment Works and a transportation system which is illustrated in Fig. 4 below:

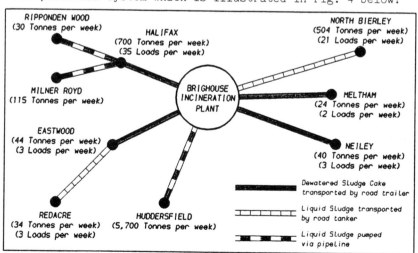

FIG 4   CALDER VALLEY TRANSPORTATION NETWORK

26. Sludges produced at the Huddersfield works of Brighouse, Deighton, Cooper Bridge and Heaton Lodge are pumped to the incineration plant. As part of the scheme some 6km of transfer main was laid to supplement existing pipelines. Separate mains were provided for the primary, humus and activated sludges. These sludges arrive on site with a dry solids content of 0.5 to 1.0% and are transferred direct to six continuous gravity thickening tanks. The combined thickened sludge is then pumped to a balancing tank before dewatering. Sludge produced at the North Bierley works and other minor works is thickened and then transferred to Brighouse by road tanker. The sludge is discharged to a below-ground collection well before being transferred at a near continuous rate to the thickened sludge balancing tank for intimate mixing with the sludges thickened on the Brighouse site.

27. As part of this scheme both gravity and mechanical thickening plant and dewatering plant consisting of two membrane plate presses were installed at the Halifax works of North Dean. The North Dean site acts as a sludge treatment centre for the Halifax area and sludges produced at Halifax and the nearby minor works are dewatered here prior to being transported by road to the incineration plant at Brighouse. On arrival the sludge cake is tipped into one of two collection hoppers within the cake handling building. The cake is then transferred by conveyor to cake storage silos before being combined with the sludge cake produced on site. Fig 5 illustrates the flow of sludges through the thickening and dewatering processes on the Brighouse site.

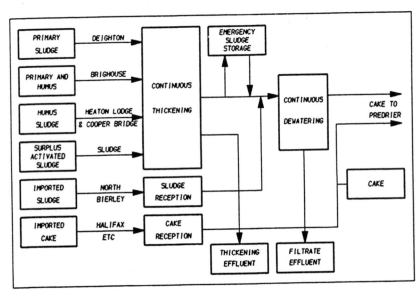

FIG 5   SLUDGE AND CAKE TRANSFERS THROUGH THE BRIGHOUSE SITE

28. During normal operation the storage of thickened sludge is kept to a minimum since excessive storage periods adversely effect its dewatering characteristics. During shutdown of the incinerator for both routine and emergency maintenance, or during periods of high sludge production, a series of eight storage tanks have been installed. These storage tanks provide storage of up to 20 days at design throughput. Once normal incineration resumes then the stored sludge is transferred to the thickened sludge balancing tank before dewatering and incineration.

29. In the event of abnormal situations which require shutdowns of the incinerator for more than 20 days, emergency cake discharge facilities have been provided to allow thickened sludge to be dewatered and the sludge cake transported off site for disposal elsewhere.

30. The sludge cake silos provide a storage period of up to 3 days for the sludge cake imported to site. During shutdown of the incinerator sludge cake is transported elsewhere and other disposal routes used.

31. The design of the dewatering, drying and incineration plant is similar to that at Esholt and Blackburn Meadows. The plant comprises four belt press type dewatering units, a thermal cake drying plant, an incinerator with a kiln diameter of 4.4m containing some 15 tonnes of sand, heat recovery unit and a gas cleaning train culminating in a 65 metre stack. The heat recovery unit has been increased in relative size to give an exit temperature of 220°C and the plant was designed to meet stack emissions principally based on Ta Luft 1986.

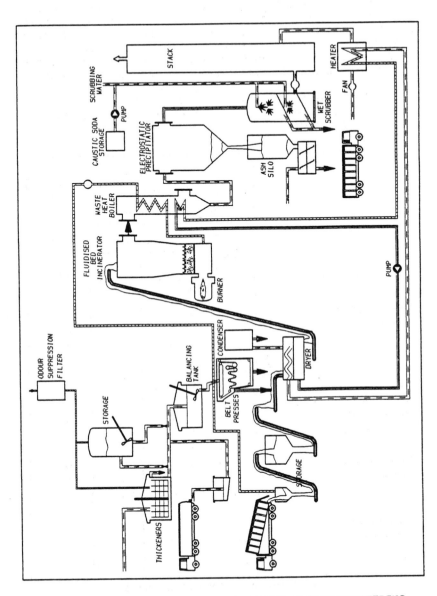

FIG 6 SCHEMATIC OF CALDER VALLEY SLUDGE DEWATERING
AND INCINERATION PLANT

32. The plant was commissioned in February 1993 and passed it's performance tests with ease with the exception of the stack emission guarantee for SOx. A mean emission level of 137 mg/m³ was achieved as compared to the 100 mg/m³ given in TA Luft 1986 and set in the contract. However, this compares favourably to both IPR 5/11 and the plant authorisation limit for SOx of 300 mg/m³. Further tests are being carried out to find the optimum operating regime for the flue gas system.

33. The results of the plant stack emission tests are given in Table 2 below and are compared to the contract guarantees and IPR5/11.

Measured Substance in Stack Emissions	RELEASE CONCENTRATIONS (as dry gas, STP, 11% O_2)			
	Calder Valley Emissions			IPR5/11 Stand-ards
	Design Limits	Measured		
		Test 1	Test 2	
Carbon Monoxide	100	3.1	3.4	50
Organic Compounds (expressed as Carbon)	20	1.5	0.7	20
Total Dust	30	2.65	1.78	20
Metals:				
-Hg	) 0.2	0.113	0.111	0.1
-Cd	)in total	0.036	0.003	0.1
-Other Metals (Ni+As+Pb+Cr+Cu+Sn+Mn)	5.0	2.25	0.44	1.0
Nitrogen Oxides (as NO_2)	Not guaranteed	888	556	650
Hydrogen Chloride	50	4.0	4.2	30
Hydrogen Fluoride	2	0.1	0.3	2
Sulphur Oxides (as SO_2)	100	119	154	300
Dioxins/Furans ITEQs (ng/m³)	Not guaranteed	0.159	0.103	1

TABLE 2   TABLE OF PERFORMANCE TEST RESULTS

34. The prime reason for the initial failure to achieve the guaranteed emission level for SOx was the discrepancy found between the on line instrumentation fitted to the plant and the wet chemical analysis used to establish the SOx emission for the guarantee purposes. The on line instrumentation had not been site calibrated against a wet chemical test and throughout the performance test gave readings well within the guarantee level and thus steps were not taken at the time to try and further optimise plant performance.

FUTURE PROPOSALS FOR SLUDGE INCINERATION IN YORKSHIRE

35. Work is progressing on the Knostrop sewage sludge incineration plant intended to serve the city of Leeds and currently tenders for this plant are being assessed. In line with Yorkshire Water's policy of anticipating the latest developments in environmental technology this plant has been specified to meet the Bimsch 17 emission standard.

36. Other incineration technologies are being considered and Babcock Water Engineering Ltd. have recently assisted Scottish Power in an experiment in the co-firing of sewage cake with coal slurry at the Methil Power Station. Also both Yorkshire Water and Babcock Water Engineering Ltd. are examining the possibilities of co-incineration of sewage sludge with municipal solid waste.

Performance of the uprated Leek STW with ozonation for colour removal

J. H. CHURCHLEY, BSc, MIWEM, Principal Process Development Officer,
A. J. GOUGH, CChem, MRSc, MIWEM, DMS, Senior Processes Officer,
P. A. BRADFORD, MSc, MIWEM, CBiol, MIBiol, Sewage Treatment
Manager, and N. C. EVERALL, BSc, PhD, MIFM, Quality Assessor
(Biology), Severn Trent Water Ltd

SYNOPSIS. A tightening of sanitary and colour consent conditions for the Leek STW necessitated £10 million extensions to the existing filter works. Vitox activated sludge was selected to down load the percolating filters to allow full nitrification and ozone treatment was selected for colour removal. Despite a number of post-commissioning problems, some of which are yet to be resolved, the extended plant has performed well. River chemical and biological samples show a marked improvement downstream, indicative of the improved sanitary quality of the effluent. Colour removal has been excellent though not meeting the 100% ile compliance required by the stringent consent condition.

BACKGROUND

1. The town of Leek is situated in the Staffordshire moorlands approximately 17 km north east of Stoke on Trent and 49 km to the south of Manchester. In the mid 18th century the town was well known for production of silk threads, buttons and ribbons [Ref. 1]. Together with the nearby towns of Macclesfield and Congleton, Leek became an important centre for the English silk industry. By the year 1891 the census records that 4248 people were employed in silk manufacture and dyeing. From this date there appears to have been a decline in the importance of silk and an increase in manufacture of smallware and fancy goods [Ref. 1].

2. In recent times the town has become a centre of more conventional textile industries especially of dyeing and finishing of knitted goods. Additionally a chemical manufacturing plant servicing the dyeworks produces an effluent for treatment at the STW.

3. The STW in 1975 comprised conventional inlet works with bar screens and grit separation followed by circular primary sedimentation tanks. Biological treatment was provided by percolating filters operated as alternating double filtration. Following humus settlement the effluent was discharged to the River Churnet, a major tributary of the River Dove.

4. Whilst the consent conditions were met reliably, there was concern expressed about the colour of the final effluent caused by the high proportion of dyewaste. This led to considerable research work in the mid 1970s and the

adoption of alum dosing into the feed to the primary sedimentation tanks for colour removal [Ref. 2]. Other STWs within the Severn Trent region were also affected by coloured dyewaste discharges [Ref. 3].

5. For a number of years the use of alum flocculation with primary settlement and alternating double filtration was adequate to achieve effluent consent conditions for BOD, SS and colour. However, after privatisation of the water industry in 1989 the NRA required a more stringent standard to be met by the works final effluent. The old and new standards are shown in Table I.

Table 1. Consent Conditions for Leek STW Effluent before and after April 1st 1992

Parameter	Prior to April 1st 1992	Post April 1st 1992
BOD$_5$	35 mg/l	20 mg/l
SS	45 mg/l	30 mg/l
ammN	10 mg/l	5/10 mg/l #
* Absorbance		
400 nm	0.15	0.060
450 nm	0.12	0.040
500 nm	0.12	0.035
550 nm	0.12	0.025
600 nm	0.10	0.025
650 nm	0.08	0.015

* Absorbance measured in absorbance units in a 10mm cell after pre-filtration through 0.45 micron membrane.

5 mg/l ammN in summer, 10 mg/l in winter.

6. It should be noticed that towards the end of this period the nature of the dyes used by the dyers in the town had changed to a predominantly reactive dye mixture. The current dye usage, illustrated in Fig. 1, overwhelmingly comprises reactive dyes. This shift in dye usage has been largely consumer driven with the requirements for dark and bright wash - fast colours especially on cotton goods [Ref. 4].

7. The change in dyeing practices was of fundamental importance in the achievement of the colour standard. Reactive dyes are in general less readily

Fig 1

Leek STW Dye Usage By Class

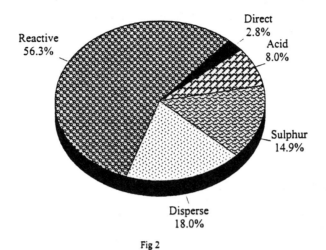

Direct
2.8%

Reactive
56.3%

Acid
8.0%

Sulphur
14.9%

Disperse
18.0%

Fig 2

Schematic Diagram of Leek Ozone Contact Tank

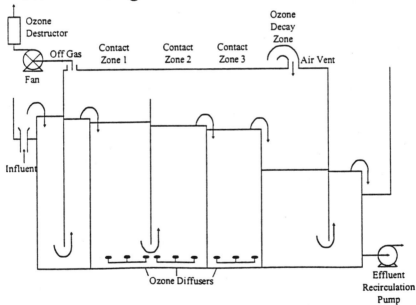

treated by coagulation with an inorganic salt [Ref. 5] and certainly alum appeared to be much less effective at Leek than formerly. In addition, the use of reactive dyes results in greater losses of dye into the dyehouse effluent [Ref. 6], these losses are compared to those in the use of other dye types in Table 2.

Table 2. Losses of dye to dyehouse effluent for different dye classes. [Ref. 6].

Dye Class	Percentage of Dye Lost in Effluent (%)
Direct	5-20
Acid	7-20
Basic	2-3
Metal complex	2-5
Sulphur	30-40
Reactive	20-50
Disperse	1-20
Vat	5-20

8. The increased quantities of dyewaste untreatable by alum dosing gave rise to high levels of colour in the sewage works effluent and failure of the colour consent conditions in 1991 and 1992.

PILOT SCALE WORK

9. In order to meet the consent conditions to be imposed on April 1st 1992 (Table 1) uprating of the biological treatment was necessary as well as the provision of an effective colour removal treatment.

10. Whilst the percolating filters were structurally sound, the organic loading was too high for complete ammonia removal even in ADF mode. However, it was felt that carbonaceous removal upstream would allow adequate nitrification to take place on the existing filter units. [Ref. 7].

11. Because the sewage contained 60% of it's dry weather sewage flow as trade effluent it was decided to carry out pilot scale trials on activated sludge systems. A BOC Vitox and a conventional surface aeration system were operated side by side in pilot scale on Leek settled sewage.

12. Aluminium sulphate dosing was implicated in high SSVI levels in both activated sludge systems. When this was stopped, the SSVIs showed a marked improvement.

13. Colour removal to the levels required by the consent conditions was problematical. There was (and still is) little in the international literature on full scale colour removal. Removal of reactive dye derived colour from the high levels experienced at Leek to the strict standards required by the NRA

therefore necessitated considerable R & D effort.

14. Chemical coagulation/ flocculation was given little consideration. Alum and other inorganics were ineffective and organic polymers for colour removal were in their infancy. Although polymers have been used in conjunction with dissolved air flotation by dyers discharging directly to river, [Ref. 8] it is likely that their consents are less strict, and they are able to selectively avoid certain troublesome dyes.

15. Chlorine and hypochlorite were avoided because of the reactivity of the chlorine species and the range of refractory organic materials likely to be present from the dyehouse and chemical manufacturing wastewaters. Formation of adsorbable organic halogens (AOX) was likely and production of highly toxic chlorinated organics was possible.

16. Tests with chlorine dioxide at Leek have shown a mixed performance. On some occasions a strong orange-yellow colour resulted which would fail the consent conditions. On other occasions, little colour removal took place at all.

17. Techniques investigated at pilot scale level were activated carbon adsorption and ozonation.

18. Packed columns of granular activated carbon were used for a pilot scale rig and were fed with coloured final effluent. Blockage with biomass occurred very rapidly and once daily backwashing was inadequate. Even with these problems of plugging, it was clear that the capacity of the carbon for colour removal was severely limited leading to very high treatment costs.

19. Subsequent trials elsewhere in the Severn Trent region with a semi-continuously washed unit have recently confirmed the very high treatment costs for colour removal.

20. Ozone has been used with some success at pilot scale for removing colour from secondary sewage effluent containing dye residue. [Ref. 9]. Nebel and Stuber report that the colour was removed by ozone to a standard of 30 ADMI (American Dye Manufacturer Institute units). (The Leek consent conditions post April 1992 equate to 49 ADMI units). To achieve the colour standard a dose of 45 mg/l was required.

21. A pilot ozone plant, obtained from Ozotech, was fed with the works final effluent. To ensure that the effluent fed to the ozone pilot plant was of as high an organic quality as the expected effluent from the extended works, the feed was filtered on a 25 micron cloth covered drum filter and was given prolonged settlement for 2-5 days retention.

22. Over a period of 6 months the required 70% colour removal was found to be achieved by an ozone dose of 9.5 mg/l in a contact period of 20 minutes. These data formed the basis of the design of the full scale ozone plant, Gough [Ref. 10].

EXTENSIONS

23. As a result of initial consideration of available treatment options, laboratory testing and pilot scale investigations the choice of BOC Vitox

activated sludge was made to provide increased biological treatment and ozonation was selected for colour removal. However, it was thought to be important to provide a balanced high quality feed to the ozone plant in order to minimise the ozone dose required. Lagoons (4 No.) were provided for storage and balancing of the ozone plant feed. Modular sand filters were also provided to give the effluent a final polish before ozone treatment.The new items of plant together with existing plant items are listed in Table 3.

Table 3. Plant units in reconstructed Leek STW flowsheet.

Item	New/ Existing	No. Units - Detail
Inlet works	Existing	
Primary sed. tanks	Existing	2 No. circular
BOC Vitox ASP Reactors	New	2 No. circular
Vitox clarifiers	New	4 No. circular
Nitrifying filters	Existing	6 No. circular
Humus tanks	Existing	4 No. circular
Lagoons	New	4 No. rectangular
Dynasand sand filters	New	20 No.
Ozone plant	New	4 No. parallel contact lanes, 2 ozone generators

24. The Vitox reactors (2 No.) were sized with a total volume of 4245 m^3 giving 7.2 hours hydraulic retention time at design DWF. With a MLSS concentration of 3.0 g/l the reactors would operate at an F/M ratio of 0.54 per day. Allowing for a load fluctuation of up to 25% above average, the installed oxygenation capacity required was 10.0 O$_2$/d.

25. Lagoons (4 No.) were provided of nominal depth 1.5 m. The total volume of 19.8 Ml gives a hydraulic retention period of 35 hours and 33 hours respectively to the design and ultimate DWF.

26. Modular sand filters (Dynasand) arranged in 4 lines each of 5 filter units were to provide final polishing before ozone treatment. A tertiary pumping station was provided to pump lagoon effluent to the sand filters and ozone plant. Each duty pump (4 duty 1 standby) provides flow to a lane of sand filter units and then to a lane of the ozone contactor. Sand filter backwash gravitates to the humus tank inlet.

27. The ozone plant comprising 2 No. ozone generators each producing up to 7.5 kg/hr of ozone from cooled, dried air. There are two air coolers and driers and each generator feeds up to two contact chamber lanes. The 4 lanes are each divided into 4 compartments. The first three of these contain diffusers to distribute the ozone into the effluent flow. The fourth chamber is an ozone decay zone to reduce the ozone residual concentration in the final effluent. A diagram showing the arrangement of the contactor chamber lanes and their compartments is given in Fig. 2.

28. The plant as described was constructed between August 1990 and September 1992 at a total cost of £10 million. Construction of the lagoons, pumping station, sand filters and ozone plant totalled £5.1 million of which £2.2 million was for the ozone plant. Fig. 3. shows the layout of the reconstructed site.

COMMISSIONING

29. The Vitox plant was commissioned by being filled with humus tank effluent which was gradually displaced by settled sewage. The existing filters were operated in the original, alternating double filtration, mode to provide sufficient BOD removal. Return activated sludge flow rate on the Vitox plant was maintained at 150% of dry weather flow.

30. In a two week period, the MLSS had risen to 2500 mg/l and substantial BOD removal was taking place. The existing percolating filters were then switched into single pass mode for nitrification which was achieved without problems and ammonia concentrations in the effluent dropped rapidly.

31. Commissioning of the Vitox plant and the adjustment in the performance of the percolating filters were achieved relatively quickly, without seeding and with a continual improvement in effluent quality.

32. The ozone plant was commissioned by Ozotech Ltd. during the Leek holiday fortnight. Colour removal performance when the dyers resumed normal working was poor and remained so throughout August and September. Ozone production tests showed that the generators were performing according to specification but off-gas analyses revealed very poor ozone utilization. Accordingly the ozone contact chambers were drained, opened up and the gas dispersion pattern observed with un-ozonised air. It was clear that gas dispersion was very poor so the units were completely drained for inspection. The problems encountered and the partial resolution are described in the next section.

POST-COMMISSIONING PROBLEMS

Ozone Plant

33. Poor ozone utilization efficiency was found to be caused by fractures in the PVC pipework carrying ozonated air to the diffusers. Fractures had all occurred at the support brackets on the inside of the concrete walls of the

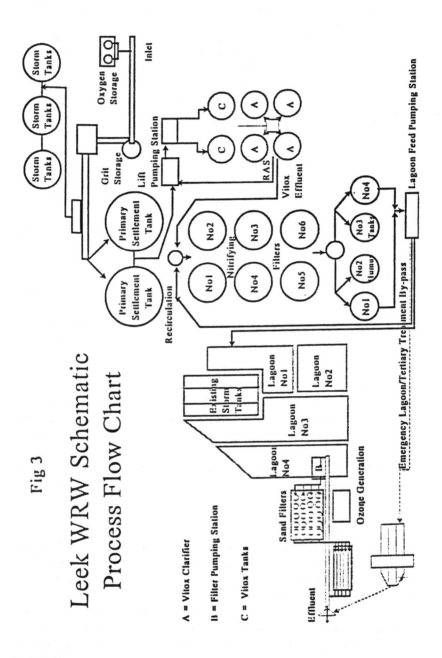

Fig 3
Leek WRW Schematic
Process Flow Chart

A = Vitox Clarifier

B = Filter Pumping Station

C = Vitox Tanks

contact chambers.

34. Damaged pipework was replaced with similar PVC material but supported with redesigned brackets. The ozone plant was re-commissioned on October 6th 1992. Subsequent colour removal has been good and is reported in the following section.

35. Ozotech Ltd. inspected the ozone installation in April 1993 and found that PVC pipework in the gallery was damaged resulting in ozone leakage. As a result the PVC pipework was replaced with stainless steel as far as the ozone diffuser manifold on one lane.

36. Important lessons learnt from this installation include the necessity for stainless steel pipework for ozonated air from generator to diffuser.

37. The ozone plant was originally fitted with diffusers comprising a PVC body and ceramic top with a PVC seal. Problems arose with breakdown of the PVC seals leading to leakage from under the ceramic top. In September 1993 these diffusers were replaced by a stainless steel body carrying a ceramic top with a stainless steel seal. At an inspection early in November 1993 a number of stainless steel welds were found to be cracked on diffusers in one of the contact chamber lanes. Remedial work is planned for January 1994.

Vitox Plant

38. During a routine inspection of the Vitox clarifiers it was found that there were problems with the sludge scrapers. A design fault in the scraper support mechanism caused scraper blades to become detached and therefore ineffective. A redesign for the blade support was agreed and remedial work completed on the 4 clarifiers over a 12 week period with no detriment to final effluent quality. No further problems have been experienced with the modified scrapers.

39. Although Vitox effluent quality was satisfactory, with expected levels of BOD and COD removal, the oxygen usage was considerably higher than expectation. Experimentation with varying the oxygen set points, the oxygen injection rate and the MLSS concentration have failed to improve on the oxygen usage. To date investigations remain on-going.

PERFORMANCE

Sanitary Parameters

40. The design philosophy for the Leek extensions requires that the Vitox activated sludge plant would effect the bulk of the BOD removal. This would enable the filters to achieve the required ammonia oxidation despite the relatively high hydraulic load.

41. The Vitox plant in practice achieved the expected BOD removal and the filters proved capable of meeting the new ammonia standard without any change of medium or refurbishment. Table 4 shows the final effluent analytical data (NRA public register) for spot samples for the pre- and post-

extension 13 month periods. BOD and SS show considerable improvements from 20 to 9.5 and 17 to 7.2 mg/l respectively. Ammonia nitrogen has improved from a mean value of 5.0 to 0.93 mg/l. The effluent TON shows a greater increase than expected. This may have been due to denitrification in the heavily loaded ADF filters prior to works extensions.

42. Consent failures for sanitary parameters are of course much reduced. Prior to extensions in the 13 month period 1/8/91 to 31/8/92, breaches of consent were as follows:

Parameter	Number of failures
BOD	11
SS	2
ammN	12

Since completion of extensions, there have been 2 failures (both for SS) in 102 samples taken.

43. The improvement in sanitary quality of the final effluent has had a beneficial effect on the River Churnet. Table 5 shows results of NRA analyses of samples upstream and downstream of the works effluent discharge for the period pre- and post- commissioning of the extensions. Clearly the downstream data shows an improvement post-extensions, with a rise in dissolved oxygen and marked reductions in BOD, (47%), TOC, (28%) and ammN (69%). Comparison of upstream and downstream data would suggest that the works effluent improves the quality of the Churnet at least for the parameters dissolved oxygen, BOD and ammonia.

Colour

44. Key to the successful performance of the extended plant is the colour removal achieved by the ozone plant. Table 6 shows final effluent absorbance values (10 mm cell against distilled water and after 0.45 micron filtration) for pre- and post- extension 13 month periods. There has been an significant improvement in absorbance values especially at 500 nm.

45. Consent failures for colour were reduced from 11 pre-extension to 5 post-extension. It should be noted that the 5 failures correspond to relatively minor breaches of the absorbance conditions e.g. 0.062 and 0.063 at 400 nm compared to 0.060 standard. These and other failures were caused by an increasing colour intensity "wave" or "front" moving through the plant. The ozone dose is set manually in a morning to give colour removal which is more than adequate to achieve the colour standards. If the colour intensity increases between the morning setting and the midday check, then failures can result.

46. An on-line absorbance monitor will be used, after performance testing to control the ozone dose automatically. This should result in a reduced ozone dose and reduced likelihood of consent failure.

47. On-site colour analysis is carried out at Leek on the lagoon effluent and the final effluent (i.e. before sand filters and ozone, and after ozone). A typical strongly coloured lagoon effluent (February 1993 monthly average) and a weakly coloured (July 1993 average) are shown in Fig. 4. Also plotted are the works effluent consent conditions and a typical final effluent absorbance graph (February 1993 average). The plateau at 450-500 nm is well illustrated in both lagoon effluent curves. This plateau is completely removed by the ozone treatment.

River Biological Surveys

48. Whilst chemical samples give at best a snap-shot of the situation at the time of sampling and then only for the parameters measured, biological surveys indicate the mean water quality over the period between surveys and are sensitive also to episodic pollution events.

49. Biological samples in the River Churnet are taken upstream of Leek STW (Wall Bridge), immediately downstream (100m) and below the Leek Brook confluence (200-300 m downstream). Samples are taken by the NRA and by Severn Trent Water at about 3 month intervals.

50. Results of biological samples are plotted for the 3 sites from March 1990 to October 1993 in Fig. 5. Prior to the completion of the extensions the upstream score varied from 68 to 104 with a mean of 87. Since commissioning the extensions the upstream score has varied from 63 to 104 with a mean value of 84. Essentially the upstream quality has remained unaltered.

51. Downstream of Leek the scores have shown a marked improvement since October 1992 (completion of works extensions). At 100 m downstream the score has improved from 18 - 53 (mean 27) to 32 - 64 (mean 53). At 200-300 m downstream the improvement has been even more dramatic with scores of 22-57 (mean 36) improving to 48-105 (mean 79). On Fig. 5 the graph shows the rise in river quality approaching the upstream values.

52. The biological data are particularly encouraging since the use of ozone in sewage treatment is novel in the UK and is, as far as the authors are aware, unique worldwide for the removal of colour from textile dye residues on a sewage treatment plant. With the large number of chemical species present in such an industrial sewage it is encouraging to see no evidence of toxicity from ozonation.

Fig 4

Graph Showing 'Strong' & 'Weak' Lagoon Effluent Discharge Consent Conditions And Typical Effluent Quality

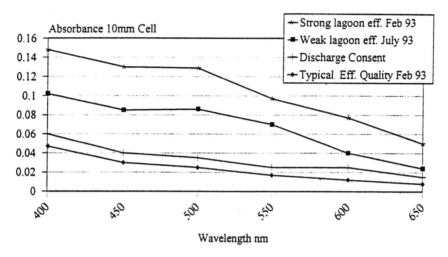

Fig. 5

NWC Biotic Score

March 1990 To October 1993 - NRA & STWL Data

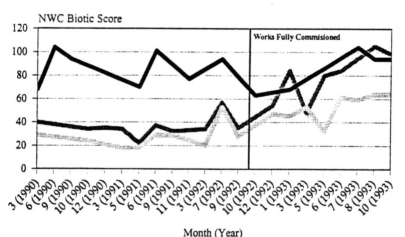

TABLE 4. Effluent quality prior to and after extensions at Leek STW (NRA data - Sanitary Analysis)

Parameter	Analytical Data (mg/l)	
	1/8/91 - 31/8/92 Pre-extensions Mean Value (maximum)	1/10/92 - 31/10/93 Post-extensions Mean Value (maximum)
BOD (+ATU) 5 day	20.2 (>55)	9.5 (19)
S.S.	16.9 (47)	7.2 (32)
AmmN.	5.0 (14)	0.93 (4.1)
T.O.N. (NO_3-N + NO_2-N)	5.1 (17.5)	12.0 (22.5)
No. Samples	57	102
No. Consent Failures	21	2

TABLE 5. Water quality in the River Churnet above and below Leek STW before and after commissioning of the extensions (NRA data)

		Pre-commissioning Leek STW 1/8/91 - 31/8/92	Post-commissioning Leek STW 1/10/92 - 31/10/93
U P S T R E A M	No. samples	13	18
	DO Conc^n. (mg/l)	10.0	9.7
	BOD (mg/l)	3.0	6.1
	TOC Filt^d. (mg/l)	6.6	6.4
	NH_3-N (mg/l)	0.30	0.53
D O W N S T R E A M	No. Samples	27	28
	DO Conc^n. (mg/l)	9.7	10.1
	BOD (mg/l)	8.9	4.7
	TOC Filt^d. (mg/l)	13.4	9.7
	NH_3-N (mg/l)	1.6	0.50

167

TABLE 6. Effluent quality prior to and after exterior at Leek STW (NRA data - absorbance values)

Parameter	Absorbance Values (10mm cell)			
	1/8/91 - 31/8/92 Pre-extensions mean value (maximum)		11/10/92 - 31/10/93 Post-extensions mean value (maximum)	
Absorbance at 400 nm	0.055	(0.199)	0.037	(0.074)
Absorbance at 450 nm	0.048	(0.175)	0.022	(0.054)
Absorbance at 500 nm	0.044	(0.174)	0.016	(0.046)
Absorbance at 550 nm	0.023	(0.100)	0.011	(0.030)
Absorbance at 600 nm	0.016	(0.068)	0.0066	(0.022)
Absorbance at 650 nm	0.0089	(0.034)	0.0048	(0.015)
No. samples	49		55	
No. consent failures	11		5	

CONCLUSIONS

53. The requirement to remove colour at Leek has provided a unique challenge which has been met with the novel use of ozonation. Not surprisingly some difficulties have been encountered, and some of these have yet to be resolved.

54. Despite the problems with the Vitox clarifiers, the extended plant has performed well and has complied readily with the tightened sanitary consent conditions.

55. Chemical analyses of river samples indicate a significant improvement in the downstream water quality with the commissioning of the works extensions.

56. In spite of the problems with ozone diffusers the colour removal has been good and mean final effluent absorbances have been inside the required consent conditions. Rapid changes in colour intensity have caused infrequent colour failures, but the proposed automation of the ozone dose is expected to minimise these occurences.

57. Biological samples since commissioning of the Leek extensions indicate a large improvement in downstream river water quality. In particular at 200-300m dowbstream the water quality has improved to that of the river upstream.

REFERENCES

1. UNIVERSITY OF LONDON INSTITUTE OF HISTORICAL RESEARCH. The Victoria history of the counties of England. A history of Staffordshire Volume III, Ed. Pugh, R.B., University Press Oxford, 1967.
2. HARKNESS, N. & JEDSON, J.D. The removal of colour from the final effluent from Leek Water Reclamation Works. Severn Trent WA. R & D project report RT19, 1975.
3. WATERS, B.D. Treatment of dyewaste. Water Pollution Control, 1979, 78, p. 12-26.
4. LOCKERBIE, M. The origin and composition of textile trade effluent. IWEM symposium "Textile Industry Trade Effluents", September 22nd, 1993, Stoke on Trent.
5. KOPRIVANAC, N., BOSANAC, G., GRABARIC, Z. & PAPIC, S. Treatment of wastewaters from dye industry. Environmental Technology, 1993, 14, No. 4., p. 385-390.
6. LAING, I.G. The importance of the effluent regulations on the dyeing industry. Society of Dyers & Colourists. Review of progress in colouration, 1991, 21, p. 56-71.
7. ACER ENGINEERING LTD. Leek water reclamation works extensions. Design stage 1 Report., November, 1990.
8. ANON. Sophisticated steel. Industrial Waste Management, November, 1992, p.22.
9. NEBEL, C. & STUBER, C. Ozone decolorisation of secondary dye-laden effluents. Second International Symposium on Ozone Technology, Montreal, 1976, p. 336-358.
10. GOUGH, A. The use of ozone to remove colour from wastewater, International Ozone Association Conference, April 1993, Berlin.

Biological nutrient removal — retrofit solutions in the UK. Design snags, operational problems and costs

P. COOPER, WRc Swindon, J. UPTON, Severn Trent Water,
Development Group, M. SMITH, WRc Swindon, and J. CHURCHLEY,
Severn Trent Water, Development Group

SYNOPSIS. The EC Urban Waste Water Treatment Directive
1991 will lead to some UK Sewage Treatment Works having to
remove Nitrogen and Phosphorus. The paper reviews the
basic biological processes available for retrofitting
existing activated sludge plants to achieve this removal
and then points to some of the problems encountered with
these processes in other countries. The authors make
suggestions as to how these problems can be overcome in
design and operation. The paper closes with a cost
comparison of different ways of up-rating an existing
nitrifying activated sludge plant to achieve
nitrification/denitrification and phosphorus removal.

INTRODUCTION

1. The European Community Urban Waste Water Treatment
Directive of 1991 (UWWTD)(ref.1) contains standards to be
achieved for Total Nitrogen and Total Phosphorus for
effluents from sewage works of 10,000 pe and above. This
will require some plants in the UK to be uprated to remove
one or both of those nutrients for the first time.

2. The UWWTD allows the national authorities to choose
from two alternative methods of implementing nutrient
removal requirements for discharges to "sensitive waters".
It is possible to decide to remove 80% of Total Phosphorus
and/or 70 to 80% of the Total Nitrogen from the defined
area or to achieve the following concentration standards on
an **annual mean basis.**

Table 1.

SIZE OF WORKS	Total P	Total N
>10,000 pe <100,000	2 mg P/l	15 mg N/l
>100,000 pe	1 mg P/l	10 mg N/l

3. The UK has decided to implement the Directive by
using the concentration standards since this is in line

with its long-established policy of setting the standard appropriate to the receiving water and its use.

4. It is generally accepted that the limiting nutrient for freshwater environments is phosphorus whereas nitrogen is the limiting nutrient in estuarine and marine environments. However, nitrogen is important for other reasons for inland streams, lakes and reservoirs where water is abstracted for water supply and the removal of nitrate becomes necessary.

5. The National Rivers Authority (NRA), Scottish River Purification Boards (RPBs) and DoE, Northern Ireland currently set standards for BOD, SS, $NH_3.N$ (not in all cases) and Total P (in some cases where the effluent goes to a receiving water which could become eutrophic). It is not common to have one for Nitrate or Total Nitrogen, but some works already have targets for nitrates in order to protect rivers used for potable supply. Consents specifying Total P are not common and are largely confined to the following areas.

i) the area of the Norfolk Broads in East Anglia (Anglia Water area),
ii) the Lake District (North West Water's area),
iii) rivers draining to Lough Neagh in Northern Ireland.

6. All together there are 23 works which currently do Phosphorus removal, all by chemical means. These are all small works. Chemical dosing to remove P is the most cost effective method for small works but for larger plants biological phosphorus removal becomes more attractive and it has the major benefit that it does not produce additional sludge. Chemical dosing can lead to an increase of 20%. Hence there is considerable interest in the use of Biological Nutrient removal for the larger works.

EXPERIENCE SO FAR WITH NUTRIENT REMOVAL

7. Nitrogen Removal The authors recently reviewed the situation in the UK(ref.2). The current paper concentrates on activated sludge processes. The first significant work on nitrogen removal in the UK was the pioneering work on nitrification in the activated sludge process done by Downing, Painter and Knowles(ref.3) at Water Pollution Research Laboratory, Stevenage. This work in the late 1950's and early 1960's established the conditions necessary for reliable operation of an activated sludge process to achieve complete nitrification. Without this excellent work much of the later work throughout the World on denitrification and biological phosphorus removal would not have been possible.

8. Work at Stevenage (pilot scale) and Rye Meads STW (full-scale) in the period 1973-6(ref.4) built on that work

and the ideas of Ludzack and Ettinger(ref.5) and Barnard(ref.6) to produce the first activated sludge denitrification system in the UK. This work was necessary to protect the River Lee (the source for 20% of London's potable water) from high nitrate concentrations. This work using a single anoxic zone (Figure 1) produced a reduction of 50% in the oxidised nitrogen being emitted from Rye Meads STW and kept the River Lee below the WHO/EC recommendations of 11.3 mg NO_3-N/l. (50 mg NO_3/l).

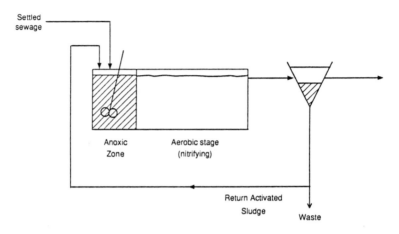

Figure 1   Conventional pre-denitrification system

9. Since this early work many more activated sludge plants have been fitted with anoxic zones. It is now regarded as standard practice for nitrifying activated sludge plants and it is not reported in the literature. The number of plants fitted with anoxic zones is not known but it must be approaching a hundred.

10. The group from WRc and Thames Water involved in the single anoxic zone work at Rye Meads took the process further still (ref.7) by the use of two anoxic zones with settled sewage being step-fed to the first anoxic zone (60%) and the second anoxic zone (40%) Figure 2.

11. This system which has the potential for 80% removal of nitrate achieved 70% (down to 11.8mg NO_3.N/l) and an overall removal of nitrogen of 78% from the strong settled sewage, 69mg Kj-N/l down to 15.4mg Total N/l. Since this work in 1976 the sewages in UK have become weaker and it is likely that the two anoxic zone system would meet the requirement for >100,000 pe of 10mg Total N/l. The 2 anoxic zone system has not been used on a full-scale in the UK but it may be used in the next 5 years to meet tighter standards. Recent work in France(ref.8) have taken this

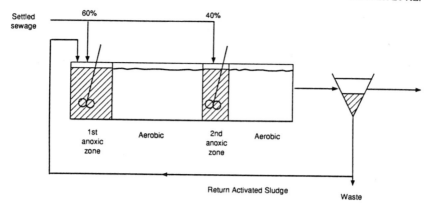

Figure 2   2 stage nitrification/denitrification

further with the use of step-feeding to three anoxic zones. They claim it to be the most cost-effective method of denitrification since it makes maximum use of the organic carbon present in the sewage whilst re-using oxygen from the nitrate. The alternative to step-feeding is recycle of mixed liquor to the anoxic zone. This can achieve the level of denitrification needed but may lead to sludge bulking since it takes the process configuration away from "plug-flow" towards the "completely mixed" regime which is more prone to bulking.

12.   Biological Phosphorus Removal   There are two main forms of biological phosphorus removal plants.

i)   Main-Stream Processes where all the P is removed in the waste sludge stream of a plant containing anaerobic, anoxic and aerobic stages. This produces a plant which is larger than the conventional nitrifying activated sludge plant.

ii)   Side-Stream P Removal Processes of the PhostripR type where the phosphorus is stripped biologically from a proportion of the sludge stream (the "side stream"), the released P is then locked-up chemically and the stripped sludge is returned to the plant to take up more P. The existing treatment units are retained and not expanded in size.

13.   Figures 3, 4 and 5 are examples of the mainstream processes. Bardenpho (Phoredox), UCT and JHB processes.

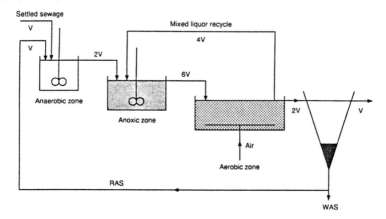

Figure 3   Bardenpho arrangement

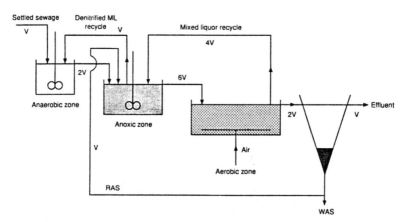

Figure 4   UCT/VIP arrangement

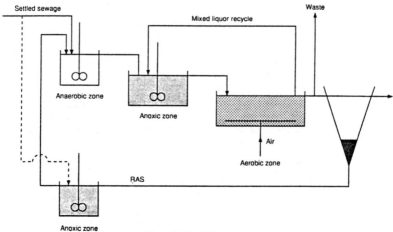

Figure 5   The JHB process

14. Figure 6 shows the side-stream Phostrip[R] processes.

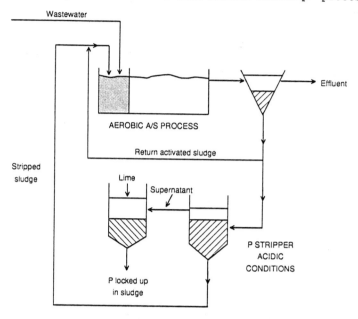

Figure 6 Phostrip[R] side stream P removal

15. In the original mainstream process the Bardenpho process(ref.9), phosphate is released from the cell biomass in the anaerobic stage and then taken up in the aerobic stage. The release of P in the anaerobic stage is caused by the take-up of volatile fatty acids by some of the bacteria. Energy is consumed in this take-up and this is derived by the hydrolysis of poly-phosphates which were stored within the cell. When these bacteria reach the aerobic stage they saturate with phosphates which are stored as poly-phosphate. The keys to the process are a) to waste the sludge in an <u>aerobic</u> state and then treat it quickly and aerobically, and b) to ensure that the anaerobic zone remains truly anaerobic (it is essential to remove any nitrate from the streams going into the anaerobic zone). Effectively the anaerobic stage acts as a selector which causes the selection of bacteria which favour phosphorus uptake. Many bacteria do this but the best known is *Acinetobacter*.

16. The Bardenpho process worked for biological P removal but tended to be unreliable and over the past 20 years a number of variants and derivatives have been produced. The main weakness of the Bardenpho process is that the recycle of return sludge is likely to contain nitrate and dissolved oxygen which can lead to the

anaerobic zone not being truly anaerobic. This is overcome
in the UCT/VIP (University of Cape Town/Virginia Initiative
Process) processes (Fig.4) by passing the return sludge to
the anoxic stage and then pumping on equal volume of
(denitrified) mixed liquor back to the anaerobic stage.
WRc have completed pilot plant trials of the UCT process
and Bardenpho arrangements for a group of Water Companies
(ref.10).

17. Another alternative method of protecting the
anaerobic stage is the use of the JHB (Johannesburg)
Process. In this process (Fig.5) the return sludge is
denitrified prior to the anaerobic stage in an extra anoxic
zone. The requirement for a carbon source for the
denitrification process is sometimes covered by feeding a
small fraction of the settled sewage to this anoxic ozone.

PROBLEMS ENCOUNTERED IN OTHER COUNTRIES
18. It is important to emphasise the lack of operational
and design experience of BNR systems in the United Kingdom
and the authors have taken this into account when
establishing the following areas of design and operational
difficulty. For the water companies embracing BNR
technology in the future the fundamental pitfalls of
nitrifying activated sludge systems including; control of
sludge age, recycle streams and oxygen input, the authors
consider to be well learnt and have restricted their points
to BNR-related problems new to the UK industry.

19. The authors' view on what constitutes a BNR design
and operational problem is based on visits to operational
plant overseas, pilot plant studies in the UK for the last
3 years, and not least an awareness that the regulating
regime currently existing in the UK, requires a high degree
of consent compliance, a factor not always appreciated by
practitioners.

a) STORM FLOWS AND WEAK SEWAGE
20. Efficient P release occurs in the anaerobic zone of
a BNR plant and effective denitrification in the anoxic
zone when sufficient readily-biodegradable carbon or BOD is
present.

21. It is accepted practice that a BOD:P ratio of at
least 20 is required in the anaerobic zone for good P
release, and historically research workers at the City of
Johannesburg, South Africa proposed that simple
carbonaceous substrates (principally Volatile Fatty Acids
or VFAs) were required by the P bacteria for consistent
performance.

22. Weak sewage and in particular periods of storm flow
become critical factors for BNR systems, creating
conditions of reduced HRT and insufficient substrate to

trigger P release in the anaerobic zone.

23. Many of the UK urban sewerage systems are of the old combined type where flows to full treatment can reach 2.5 to 3 x Dry Weather Flow (dwf) during minimal rainfall.

24. <u>Solutions - Flow Balancing</u> The peaks of hydraulic excess can be balanced with sufficient tankage and flows regulated to the BNR system. These flow balancing tanks provide also a useful buffer for the return of high Ammonia (>500 mg/l) waste streams from the sludge processing facility.

25. The requirement for flow balancing is not confined to the UK and the new BNR scheme under design for the City of Johannesburg at the Johannesburg Northern Works incorporates balance tanks of 6 hrs dwf capacity (ref.11).

26. <u>VFA addition</u> Sufficient short chain fatty acids (VFAs) are necessary to trigger the biological P release process, and a great deal of development activity has taken place in S. Africa and Canada to develop on-site methods of VFA production in order to provide the desired concentration of VFA in the Anaerobic reactor. Pre-fermentation of primary sludge in an on-site fermenter has been established as a fundamental requirement for most BNR designs, required to remove 90% of the available P.

27. There are a number of fermenter designs available (ref.12) and an example of a separate fermenter and sludge thickener is illustrated in Fig 7.

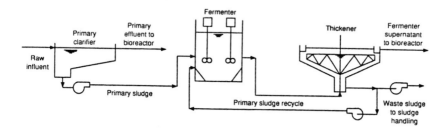

Figure 7 Separate complete mix/thickener fermenter

28.   As a "Rule-of-Thumb" 7.5 mg/l of VFA is required to release 1 mg/l P in the anaerobic zone and typically "normal strength" UK sewage contains 15-40 mg/l VFA and so considerable quantities of injected VFA are required.

29.   Oldham(ref.13) reports that recent designs for on-site fermenters in Montana USA are capable of producing injected streams with VFA concentrations of 400 mg/l VFA. These fermenters have a sludge retention of more than 12 days and when the withdrawn sludge is finally pumped to the sludge digesters a reduction in sludge gas generation of 30% is experienced as a result of this fermentation stage.

30.   The authors experience with UK pilot plant studies has emphasised the need for VFA injection. Work at WRc Swindon (ref.10) showed that successful P release and stable control of the process could be achieved by small additions of acetic acid. It should be noted that it may not be necessary to dose acetic acid continually but to allow for its switch-on during wet weather periods as a control measure. The extra sludge operated by this procedure will be very small and much less than for instance created by the addition of Ferric or Ferrous salts. More recently, reported work in the UK by Severn Trent at Hinckley showed the importance of VFA addition to both mainstream UCT and side-stream Phostrip[R] pilot plants removing Phosphate from a typical UK sewage with a BOD:P ratio of 15 (ref.14).

31.   The UK industry is familiar with the operation of continuously-fed gravity thickeners which form the basis for the design of VFA fermenters and as such this concept should not provide too many obstacles. Because of the long SRT of these purpose-designed fermenters they will need to be covered and odours vented to an odour treatment system, unlike many of the existing primary sludge thickeners which remain uncovered.

(b)   Effluent Solids and Tertiary Treatment
32.   Given the necessary conditions for good P release recent reported pilot studies in the (refs 10, 14) show that both mainstream processes (UCT) and sidestream Phostrip[R] are capable of producing effluents of less than 1 mg/ Tot P. However, in a nutrient removal process the Phosphorus is bound up with the sludge and it is therefore important to keep suspended solids in the effluent to a minimum if low level P consents are to be achieved.

33.   Good solids retention is essential in the clarifier, and since the phosphorus content of the solids is approximately 5% an effluent containing 10 mg/l SS will contain 0.5mg/l Tot P in the solids. This relationship is illustrated in Figure 8.

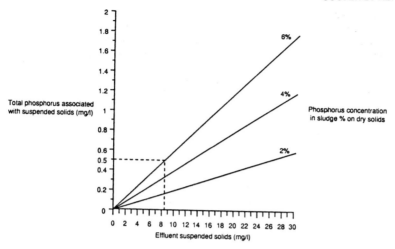

**Figure 8 Effect of effluent suspended solids concentration
on total P in effluent**

34. <u>Solutions</u> Almost certainly UK BNR plants required
to meet standards of 1.0 mg/l Tot P or less, will require
the provision of tertiary filtration, and the authors
consider that clarifier design is particularly important
with upward flow velocities not exceeding 0.8 m/hr thus
ensuring good solids capture.

(c) <u>STABLE FOAMS AND SLUDGE QUALITY</u>
35. The incidence of sludge bulking appears to be common
in nutrient removal plants but there is recent reported
evidence from the UK (refs.10,14) that BNR systems can
produce good settling sludges (SSVI 80 to 120 ml/g)
comparable with conventional activated sludge system.

36. The mechanisms of low F/M filamentous bulking in BNR
systems are unclear but the significant unaerated fractions
of the sludge inventory in a BNR plant associated
principally with the Anaerobic and Anoxic reactors provides
the conditions to support sludge bulking. The careful
control of dissolved oxygen levels are necessary to achieve
effective denitrification but this can create oxygen
deficient zones promoting the proliferation of low D.O.
filaments such as *Microthrix sp.*

37. The early design plans particularly in S. Africa had
extensive Anaerobic zones with an HRT's of >3 hrs. These
often underloaded plants provided an unnecessary large
unaerated sludge mass with consequent filamentous bulking,
and these filamentous sludge organisms manifest themselves
as a floating scum or stable foam. These foams are trapped
behind the internal baffle walls of the reactor and can
stabilise to dramatic levels until leaking into the final

clarifier and contaminating the effluent.

38. The authors' experience of visiting plants in both North America and South Africa is that stable foam formation is a very common feature of BNR systems.

Solutions

Sludge Bulking

39. <u>Minimise unaerated fraction</u> A "rule-of-thumb" recommends that the unaerated sludge fraction should not exceed 40% and more recent designs for BNR plants with supplementary VFA addition have a smaller Anaerobic zone (10% reactor volume) which helps to reduce the unaerated mass fraction. Maintenance of a high Readily Biodegradable COD/BOD (RBCOD) concentration in the feed to the Anaerobic/Anoxic reactors reduces the propensity for sludge bulking.

Stable Foams

40. <u>Sub-surface baffles</u> Historically the early designs incorporated above surface baffles separating the reactor zones and effectively trapping these stable foams. Despite the fact that baffles are required to prevent back-mixing between zones sub-surface baffles should be designed as cascades between reactors with 2-3 cm head loss ensuring that scums and foams are transported through the reactor to the clarifier.

41. <u>Clarifier scum removal</u> A robust and effective surface scum removal system is needed which may incorporate an adjustable beach providing the possibility of continuous positive scum removal. It is important that these scums are transported out of the sludge inventory to the sludge processing plant or elsewhere where these foams are unable to re-inoculate the BNR sludge.

42. **The authors philosophy with scum and stable foam formation in BNR plants is that it should be expected and "lived with" with careful design compensating for this phenomenon.**

(d) Stand-by Chemical Addition
43. Whilst the state-of-the-art has reached the point where reliable BNR plants can be designed and operated to perform as expected; it is still necessary to provide chemical back-up systems for phosphate removal. The failure of an aeration unit or a clarifier mechanism, a recycle pump or the breakdown of a VFA fermenter are examples of situations where supplementary chemical back-up will be required to comply with consented targets.

44. Furthermore recent research (ref.15) has shown that small supplementary dosages of metal precipitant can have a markedly beneficial effect on Biological Phosphorus removal in BNR systems. However, excessive additions of chemical as a simultaneous precipitant has been shown by Lötter, (ref.16) to have an inhibitory effect on the biological uptake of P. The control of the metallic precipitant is therefore essential for cost and optimisation of the biological pathways of P removal.

(e) RESOLUBILISATION OF P IN THE SLUDGE HANDLING AND PROCESSING STREAMS

45. In BNR processes the biologically-removed phosphates are taken up in the bacterial cells. Ideally the first stage of sludge treatment (thickening) should be aerobic so that the P remains with the thickened sludge. Under anaerobic conditions the phosphates are released to the liquid phase and after a subsequent dewatering stage the return liquors may have to be treated for chemical removal of phosphates before returning to the plant.

46. Waste sludge from a BNR plant contains typically 4 to 6% P and this sludge when anaerobically digested in the sludge digestion plant releases as much as 75% of this phosphorus into solution in the digester. Depending on the chemical balances in the digester as much as 80% of this P can be precipitated in the sludge or on the walls of the digester and pipework in the form of Struvite, Vivanite, bushite, hydroxyapatite or a variety of other precipitants.

47. Struvite (Mg NH_4 PO_4 $6H_2O$) formation and subsequent blockage of pipe work is a widespread problem in North American plants, and is almost inevitable in the presence of the high Ammonia levels found in digester liquors. Ferrous ion in the digester is precipitated as Vivanite if the levels of Phosphorus are high enough.

Solutions

48. Flotation Thickening of Waste BNR Sludge Streams The waste sludge should be thickened in such a way that the phosphates will be concentrated in as small a volume as possible. Dissolved Air Flotation thickening is ideal since it keeps the phosphorus attached to the sludge biomass and the liquid underflow from the DAF plant can be returned to the aeration basin. Flotation can thicken sludge up to 5% d.s. without polymer addition which can be important as some of the polymers used for DAF thickening are inhibitory to nitrification.

49. Struvite Formation Much research needs to be done on the exact mechanisms of Struvite formation but Randall and Knocke (ref.17) indicated that Struvite formation in primary digesters cannot be prevented as the reaction rates

are so fast.

50.   It may be necessary to chemically-treat the return liquor streams with metallic salt addition effectively precipitating this Phosphate rich liquor, and BNR plants recently designed in Holland and Belgium have this design facility of return - liquor treatment.   The Phostrip[R] Process overcomes many of the problems associated with resolubilisation of P in mainstream process designs, by using lime to precipitate the P released from the stripper tank.   The lime forms an insoluble precipitate of Calcium Hydroxy - Apatite from which <u>no</u> P is released back into solution and a number of side-stream Phostrip[R] type plants have been installed in recent years in Holland and Germany.

(f)   <u>OPERATOR TRAINING AND PLANT CONTROL</u>
51.   BNR processes are without doubt more difficult to control than conventional activated sludge processes, and in order to reduce the difficulty of operation both management and operators should be trained to a high skill level.   Training should include:

- o   mechanisms of nutrient removal
- o   sampling and monitoring
- o   use of analytical test kits
- o   fault finding procedures

52.   The use of expert systems incorporating "fault-trees" will probably be essential for operation of these plants at the low manpower levels used in the UK sewage treatment plants.

53.   In addition to operator training further development of on-line sensors is required to monitor continuously these variables which can be significant such as readily biodegradable fraction, D.O., Ammonia, Nitrate and Phosphate among others.

54.   Measurement of these variables are considered necessary to adjust the recycle streams, optimise the Anoxic/Anaerobic zones and generally measure the "health" of the process.

55.   **Hinckley Pilot Plant - Severn Trent Water**   The pilot plants operated at Hinckley were both small size units developed as a side-by-side comparison of mainstream BNR system configuration and Phostrip[R] side-stream design.   The Hinckley settled sewage contains textile effluent and is disadvantageous for Biological P removal.

56.   The flow rate of those plants ranged from 50 to 100 litres/hr but despite the small size yielded important design data some of which has been described by (refs.14 and 18) previously.

57. **Stratford Upon Avon (Milcote Works) - BNR Evaluation Facility - Severn Trent Water** This plant incorporates a conversion of an activated sludge plant into a side by side Phostrip[R] and mainstream BNR evaluation facility.

58. The mainstream BNR process has the design flexibility to be operated in a number of process configurations including the necessary recycle streams. The Phostrip[R] side stream system is designed with a pre-stripper and stripper tank and both process streams can be supplied with flows rich in VFA generated by an on-site primary sludge fermenter.

59. The sewage at Stratford contains wastes from vegetable processing and is therefore seasonally favourable for Biological Nutrient Removal. The average flow of each process stream at Stratford is 2,500 m³/d and the plant was commissioned in November 1993.

60. **Beckton Pilot Tests - Thames Water** Thames Water have recently reported (ref.19) on their evaluation of the JHB mainstream process at Beckton STW. This recently started work is being done on a small proportion of the total flow to Beckton but at 30,000m³/d it is equivalent to many full-scale works.

61. **WRc Pilot-Plant Tests** WRc (on behalf of a group of Water Companies) has done pilot plant tests with the mainstream biological P removal processes, Bardenpho and UCT, but publication of the results is currently restricted. The work demonstrated that it was possible to operate the UCT process consistently to 1mg Total P/l and demonstrated methods of control under wet weather conditions.

62. **Costs** The costs for each plant to be retrofitted will need to be assessed individually but the following will give an indication of the relative costs for a number of different methods of uprating an existing nitrifying activated sludge plant to achieve phosphorus removal by biological and chemical methods.

63. Two sizes of plant have been considered 100,000 pe (20 ML/d) and 250,000 pe (50 ML/d).
Figures 9 and 10 show the plant flow sheet before and after the addition of biological P removal. The following retrofit options were considered:-

    i)   Denitrification
    ii)   Biological P Removal using the UCT configuration with on-site VFA generation.
    iii) Biological P Removal using the UCT configuration with acetic acid dosing.
    iv)   Chemical P Removal using Ferric Sulphate as the

precipitant.
v) Chemical P Removal using Ferrous Sulphate as the precipitant.

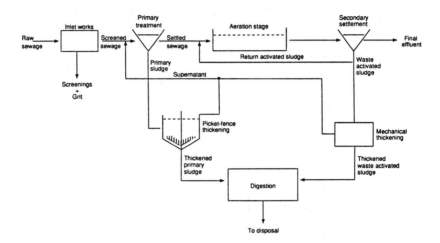

Figure 9 Nitrifying activated sludge process

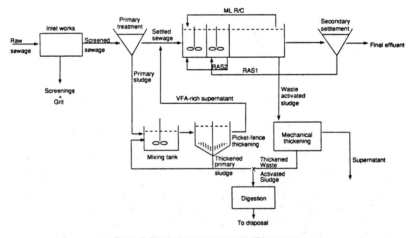

Figure 10 Biological nutrient removal with VFA generation

64. Factors used in the cost calculations. It is estimated that P removal by the addition of Iron Salts will lead to an increase in sludge production of 20% for the waste activated sludge solids.

The plant was depreciated on a 21 year period and the discount rate was 5%.

The settled sewage feed consisted of:

    180 mg BOD_5/l
     35 mg Total N/l
     30 mg NH_3.N/l
     10 mg Total P/l

The effluent target was:-

     5   mg BOD_5/l
     5   mg Total N/l
    <0.5 mg NH_3.N/l
    <1   mg Total P/l

Chemical costs used were:-

    Ferric Sulphate   £65/tonne of liquid
    Ferrous Sulphate £32.50/tonne of liquid
    Acetic Acid   £265/tonne (80% Acetic Acid)

Electricity cost 5.0p/kWh

For the options iii), iv) andv) the addition of:

    iii)   acetic acid was 25mg/l.

    iv)   ferric sulphate : 3.0 gFe^{3+}/gTP removed.

    v)   ferrous sulphate: 2.0gFe^{2+}/gTP removed.

The results of the costing exercise are shown in Table 2. The study showed that the cost of Biological P removal using VFAs generated on site from primary sludge was competitive with the addition of ferrous sulphate and the addition of acetic acid was not much more expensive. Intermittent addition of acetic acid during wet weather periods would be cheaper and may be cost competitive with on-site generation of VFAs. At the 250,000 pe scale it may be inappropriate to use Ferrous Sulphate because of the high operating costs and the reliance on large numbers of road tankers to keep the plant supplied.

Table 2 : COSTS OF NUTRIENT REMOVAL PROCESSES

No	Process Option	100,000 Population		250,000 Population	
		N.P.V (£m)	Unit Cost (p/m³)	N.P.V (£m)	Unit Cos (p/m³)
1	Nitrifying Activated sludge plant	6.14	3.34	12.31	2.68
2	Denitrifying Activated sludge plant	6.40	3.48	12.91	2.81
3	Bio-P removal with VFA generation	6.91	3.85	15.16	3.40
4	Bio-P removal with Acetic acid dose	7.92	4.31	17.73	3.86
5	Chemical P removal with Ferric Sulphate	8.86	4.82	19.67	4.28
6	Chemical P removal with Ferrous Sulphate	7.51	4.08	16.29	3.54

65. **Summary and Conclusions** Experimental work, some of
which has been undertaken by the authors, indicates that
BNR plants can be designed to work satisfactorily in the
UK. A number of design configurations are feasible and the
correct choice may require site-specific pilot work as
sewage characteristics and existing plant layout are all
important factors.

66. A whole-life cost analysis illustrates some of the
capital investment implications of BNR technology.

67. A number of significant design and operation problems
exist; the most significant being:-

a)   Storm flows leading to dilution and lack of VFAs.
b)   Stable foams/sludge bulking
c)   Resolubilisation of P in the sludge treatment plant

Potential Solutions exist to overcome these namely:-

a)   flow-balancing and VFA generation and injection into
      the Anaerobic reactor.
b)   adequate scum removal and below-surface baffles
c)   chemical pretreatment of return liquor streams or
      the use of the Phostrip[R] side stream process which
      incorporates lime and prevents the resolubilisation
      of P in the sludge treatment plant.

68.   The costs for uprating an existing nitrifying
      activated sludge plant to achieve i) denitrification
      and ii) phosphorus removal by 2 biological and 2
      chemical methods has been attempted. The study
      showed that the on-site generation of VFAs or the

part-time use of acetic acid would be cost
competitive with the use of iron salts for chemical
P removal.

REFERENCES
1.   COUNCIL OF THE EUROPEAN COMMUNITIES. Directive
concerning waste water treatment. 91/271/EEC, official
journal No. L35, 21 May 1991.
2.   COOPER, P.F., UPTON, J. and CHURCHLEY. Paper presented
to the IAWQ on Nutrient Removal held at Perugia, Italy,
June, 1993.
3.   DOWNING A.L., PAINTER H.A., and KNOWLES, G.
Nitrification in the activated sludge process. Journal of
the Institute of Sewage Purification, 1964, pp 130-158.
4.   COOPER P.F, DREW E.A., BAILEY D.A., and THOMAS E.V.
Recent advances in sewage effluent denitrification Part I.
Water Pollution Control, 76, (3), 1977, pp 287-300.
5.   LUDZACK F.J. and ETTINGER M.B. Controlling operation to
minimise activated sludge effluent nitrogen. Journal of
the Water Pollution Control Federation, 34, 1962, p920.
6.   BARNARD J.L. Biological denitrification. Water
Pollution Control, 72, (6), 1973, P705.
7.   COOPER P.F., COLLINSON B., and GREEN M.K. Recent
advances in sewage effluent denitrification. Part II.
Water Pollution Control 76, (4), 1977, pp 389-401.
8.   LESOUEF A., PAYRAUDEAU M., ROGALLA F. and KLEIBER B.
Optimising nitrogen removal reactor configurations for
on-site calibration of the IAWPRC activated sludge model.
Water Science and Technology, 25, (6), 1992, pp 105-123.
9.   BARNARD J.L. Cut P & N without chemicals, Water and
Wastes Engineering, 1974, 11, (4) pp 33-36.
10. WRc Report UC-1905. Biological Phosphorus Removal in
the Activated Sludge Process - Restricted circulation.
11. PITMAN, A.R., City of Johannesburg, Personal
communication.
12. OLDHAM, W. RABINOWITZ, DAWSON, R.N. and McGEACHIE, G.
Primary sludge fermentation - Design and Optimisation for
BNR plants. Paper presented at European Nutrient Removal
Conference, Wakefield, UK, Sept 1992.
13. OLDHAM, W. University of British Columbia, Vancouver,
Canada - Personal Communication.
14. UPTON, J., CHURCHLEY, J. and FERGUSSON, A. Pilot scale
comparison of Mainstream BNR and Sidestream Phostrip[R]
systems for Biological removal of nutrients. Paper
presented at WEF conference at Anaheim, USA, October 1993.
15. WILSON, A.W., STEVENS, G.M. and BO, P.
Retrofitting Biological Nutrient Removal Processes at
Existing Wastewater Treatment Facilities. Proc. European
Conference on Nutrient Removal Wakefield Sept. 1992.
16. LOTTER, L.H. Combined chemical and biological removal
of Phosphate in Activated Sludge Plants. Water Science and
Technology, 1991, 23, Kyoto, p.611.
17. RANDALL, C.W. and KNOCKE, W.R. The formation of
Phosphorus precipitates during the anaerobic digestion of

high phosphate activated sludge. Report prepared for Air Products and Chemicals Inc. USA. - Abstracted for Nutrient Workshop - WEF Conference Anaheim, October, 1993.
18. UPTON, J. and FARRIMOND, M. (1993). A strategy to meet the Nutrient (N & P) standards of the Urban Waste Water Directive, Water Science Technology 27, 1993, pp 297-306.
19. WILLIAMS, S. and WILSON, A.W. Design, Commissioning and Operation of the Beckton Biological Nutrient Removal Plant. Paper presented to the IWEM, Scientific Section Seminar, London, May, 1993.

ACKNOWLEDGEMENTS

The authors wish to thank WRc and Severn-Trent Water for permission to publish this paper. The views expressed are those of authors and do not necessarily represent those of WRc or Severn-Trent Water.

Strathclyde sewage sludge disposal: the solution is recycling

Professor T. A. ANDERSON, FICE, FIWEM, FIOSH, FIMgt, Director of Sewerage, Strathclyde Regional Council, and M. C. BAILEY, MSc, MICE, MIWEM(DipWEM), Associate and Divisional Manager, Montgomery Watson Ltd

SYNOPSIS.   Strathclyde Regional Council disposes of 60 000 tDS (tons of dry solids) of sewage sludge per year from a population of 2.3 million. 95% of the sludge is disposed of at sea in a prescribed area, but this practice must cease by the end of 1998.   Compliance with the Urban Waste Water Treatment Directive (UWWTD) (91/271/EEC) will also require construction of sewage treatment works at several coastal communities, and increased standards of treatment at others. The combined effects of these requirements will increase the raw sludge quantities to 95 000 tDS/year. A recent study has evaluated sludge treatment and disposal alternatives for the large quantities of sludge involved.

BACKGROUND

1.   Strathclyde Region, as the gaelic name implies (strath being the anglicised form of srath, meaning valley) is centred on the River Clyde which

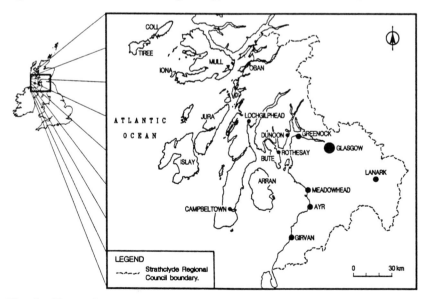

Fig. 1. The study area

drains part of the central belt of Scotland westwards to the Atlantic Ocean. The Region includes the Glasgow conurbation together with coastal communities from Oban in the north to Ayr and Girvan in the south. It also includes the islands of the Inner Hebrides.

2.   The River Clyde has supported development on the western side of the central belt of Scotland and evidence of the area's industrial past stretches from Greenock and Port Glasgow in the west through Dumbarton, Paisley, Glasgow city and Dalmarnock to Motherwell in the east. Much regeneration has taken place and communications are good.

3.   Glasgow and the neighbouring communities of Renfrewshire and Lanarkshire are well served by sewage treatment works but the coastal communities in the west are still generally without sewage treatment facilities. Although approximately 4 000 tDS/yr of liquid sludge are utilised in agriculture, in Lanarkshire and Ayrshire, all of the sewage sludge from the Glasgow conurbation is disposed of at sea in a designated location south of Garroch Head on the Island of Bute. Two sludge vessels operate five days a week from the two largest sewage treatment works along the Clyde (Shieldhall and Dalmuir). 1.7 million wet tonnes per year or approximately 50 000 tDS/yr are disposed of by this means.

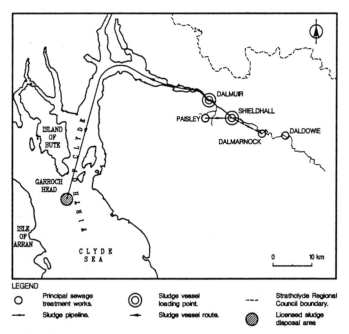

Fig. 2. Existing marine disposal of sewage sludge

4.   Sea disposal has been practised by Strathclyde Regional Council and its predecessors since 1904 and, although it is mainly untreated sludge which is disposed of to sea, this has in the past been considered a satisfactory means of disposal.

190

5.   However, at the 1990 North Sea Conference the UK Government pledged to phase out the disposal of sewage sludge at sea and this commitment was included in the 1991 UWWTD.   Strathclyde therefore decided to review their sludge disposal policy and initiate a sludge strategy study.

6.   The Study included the whole Region but the main part involved finding alternatives to the sea disposal operation.   However, the Council included in the brief the requirement for a full Environmental Impact Assessment (EIA) of the existing sea disposal method.

7.   The importance of environmental aspects was further emphasised by the requirement for a BPEO (Best Practicable Environmental Option) methodology to be used.

OBJECTIVES AND METHODOLOGY

8.   The Regional Council's objectives for the study were :

(a)   To establish the environmental impact of the present method of sludge disposal at sea, south of Garroch Head;

(b)   To identify the best alternative method using the BPEO methodology.

(c)   To compare the best alternative method with the existing method.

9.   The BPEO methodology recommends that a number of sequential tasks be undertaken.   It involves a rigorous review of sludge treatment and disposal possibilities and emphasises the environmental effects.   Operational security is also important but costs are relegated in importance and dealt with under the BATNEEC principle; Best Available Technology Not Entailing Excessive Cost.

10.   A methodology was developed which included the BPEO technique but was specific to the requirements of Strathclyde.   This involved the submission of Working Papers at key dates within the programme.   These were discussed and agreed with the Council's Officers.   In addition, an integral part of the methodology was establishment of a Peer Review Group to review and comment on the Working Papers and study findings.   The Group consisted of three eminent university Professors with specialist expertise relevant to the Study.   *"The Peer Review Group considered all of the Working Papers and concluded that the study had been approached in a strictly professional manner, taking into account the issues of technical, environmental, financial and legal factors.   The final strategy arrived at is considered by the Peer Review Group to be the best practicable environmental option.   The most important concern of all is the fact that the study allows for the re-use of sewage sludge in a satisfactory way.   It allows the disposal authority to develop a regenerative approach which in the opinion of the Peer Review Panel, will enable progress to be made towards a sustainable system".*

11.   Because of the size of the Region, the relative location of sludge sources and the large differences in sludge quantities, the Study was broken down into four sets of activities.

12.   Following the "data collection" and "assessment of quantities and

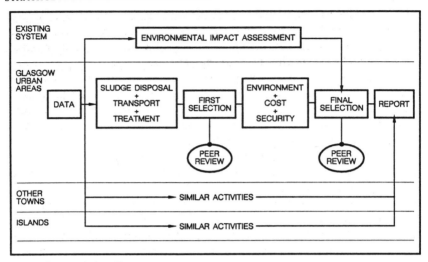

Fig. 3. Activity diagram

nature of sludge", the initial engineering activity was a "land use review" which involved the identification and quantification of potential disposal outlets. These included forestry, agriculture, landfill and land reclamation. In parallel with the land use investigations, the logistics and practicalities of transportation were studied, the sludge treatment methods considered possible in the study area were reviewed and outline design criteria established.

13. Results of the three parallel lines of investigation were then brought together with the consideration of disposal, treatment and transport options for each source of sludge.

14. A first selection of preferred options, carried out using a number of criteria, produced a short list of options for more detailed consideration and these were engineered for the specific sites. The most likely schemes were then reviewed in the light of environmental, cost, and operational security aspects, and a discussion/decision matrix was prepared from which a preferred sludge strategy was identified. Environmental considerations featured extensively at both selection stages.

15. The study has addressed the sludge treatment and disposal requirements for sludges arising within the Strathclyde Region up to the year 2011 planning horizon.

LEGISLATIVE REQUIREMENTS

16. A thorough review of relevant Scottish, UK and European Community legislation was carried out. The legislation is both extensive and complicated. Some of it overlaps and has implications in a number of different areas. The production, treatment, transport and disposal of sewage sludge is subject to strict control and monitoring procedures, which are likely to become even stricter as further environmental legislation is promulgated.

17. Regulatory requirements determine the extent and type of sewage treatment required, and place restrictions on sludge disposal methods. The quantity of sewage sludge arising is directly affected by legislation which controls the effluent quality from sewage treatment works.

18. Some legislation encourages the beneficial use of sludge on land but other legislation may prevent land use, depending on the definition of a hazardous waste, which still has to be made clear by legislators. It has been assumed that a balance will be struck between the environmental benefits of sludge use and the prevention of pollution.

19. The principal effects of the UWWT Directive are to ban the disposal of sludge to sea by 31 December 1998 and to enforce the improved treatment of sewage from coastal towns and those works such as Dalmuir which only have primary sedimentation and discharge to inland waters. The Clyde River Purification Board will designate waters as 'sensitive', 'normal' or 'less sensitive'. This will determine the level of treatment required and will in turn affect the nature and quantities of sludge produced at each location.

NATURE AND QUANTITY OF SLUDGE

20. Sludge quantities were predicted based on estimates of population and industrial development, assuming that existing plant performance and sludge draw-off facilities will be improved to achieve the design sludge yield figures. Quantities of sludge were estimated for over 400 sewage treatment works, discharges and other sources in the study area.

21. The growth in predicted sludge production is illustrated in Fig. 4.

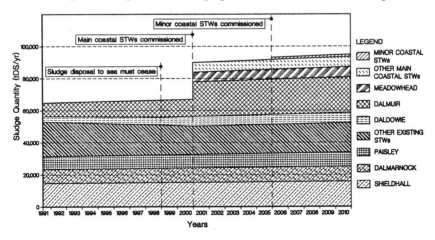

Fig. 4. Predicted sludge production

This shows that total sludge produced within the area will increase by approximately 50% within the study horizon. It also shows how the effects of legislation will drive the implementation of additional sewage treatment facilities at key dates and the need for suitable outlets for the disposal of sludge. In summary then, by the end of 1998 Strathclyde Sewerage need to find secure outlets for some 65 000 tDS/yr and two years later for 90 000 tDS/yr.

22.   The total population for the whole region was estimated as 2.35 million and the equivalent population, after taking account of pollution loads from industry, was estimated as 3.89 million.

23.   The trends in changes of populations, amount and type of industry have also been assessed. It has been assumed that although there may be local changes, the overall net effect for the Region is no significant change in population nor population equivalent, within the project horizon.

24.   The nature of the sludge produced by existing and future sewage treatment was assessed for its impact on treatment and disposal.

25.   The majority of sludges are clean enough for disposal to land but some sludges are not. Alternative treatment and disposal methods were considered for those sludges arising from contaminated sewage, whilst acknowledging that trade effluent control will continue to improve.

DISPOSAL OPTIONS

26.   Sludge disposal/re-use is the most important factor in determining the overall strategy and therefore was considered before treatment and transport. The BPEO methodology dictates that beneficial utilisation of sludge should be achieved where practicable. In addition, the Study strove to achieve the most environmentally efficient outlet that is also safe, flexible, reliable and robust in the long term. Having quantified the existing and future sludge production and the proportion of those arisings that are contaminated, the suitability and quantities of sludge for land application were assessed.

27.   Existing land uses for sludge application were identified and the operational constraints, practical considerations and application rates of sludge evaluated. The capacity of outlets to accept sludge was also quantified.

28.   From the disposal/re-use options investigated it was shown that agriculture, forestry, land reclamation and landfill have sufficient capacity to accept large quantities of sewage sludge in various forms.

29.   The seasonal variability of these disposal/re-use options means that no single option can be selected to provide a continuous outlet throughout Strathclyde, and that a combination of disposal/re-use routes should be used. Landfill has the capacity to receive all the sludge produced in the Region. However, it will only be required if and when other outlets cannot accept the quantities of sludge being produced.

30.   Such a flexible disposal/re-use approach allows for the development of alternative outlets, e.g. for sludge-amended soils, in local or regional development programmes in future years.

TREATMENT OPTIONS

31.   An extensive review of sludge treatment methods was carried out. This ranged from the simplest storage and disposal systems to technically complex incineration plants. Several new and emerging technologies such

as a deep shaft wet air oxidation technique and gasification (pyrolysis) processes were also reviewed. Each was considered in relation to the acceptability and ease of disposing of the end product, operational security, environmental impact and cost. A major consideration was the extent to which a treatment process is proven.

32. It was concluded that stabilisation of the raw sludge by anaerobic digestion (fermentation) should be the principal sludge treatment process throughout the Region. The process can be followed by thickening, dewatering and drying stages to produce an end product suitable for a number of different outlets.

33. The basic sludge treatment process train is indicated in Fig. 5 together with alternative re-use outlets.

34. Contaminated sludges can be treated by alkaline stabilisation prior to disposal in contained landfill. This will help to prevent obnoxious odours and the leaching of metal ions.

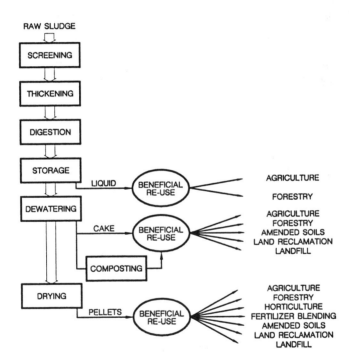

Fig. 5. Basic sludge treatment and disposal philosphy

TRANSPORT AND CENTRALISATION

35. Current methods of sludge transport used in Strathclyde were reviewed and the amount of screening and sludge thickening practised, was also noted. Centralisation of the sludge shipping operation at Shieldhall is

achieved by road transport of sludges into Shieldhall and pumping through dedicated sludge mains from Paisley and Dalmarnock sewage treatment works. The general conclusion regarding the existing transport systems was that they function satisfactorily but improvements in the operation of the tanker fleet together with thickening of sludges at source would make the road transport system more efficient.

36. The pipeline from Paisley is relatively new but the pipeline from Dalmarnock is quite old and gives rise to the occasional problems. Both pumping mains are single pipelines and the pumping operations are therefore more at risk.

37. Future requirements for sludge transport were considered and it was recommended that several new screening and thickening centres be established in order to reduce the volumes of sludge transported.

38. Centralisation of sludge treatment will help to optimise raw sludge transport, treatment and the transport to disposal.

39. It was concluded that road transport offers much greater flexibility and should continue to be the mainstay of the sludge transport system but some operational improvements should be made. In addition, some new pipelines between major sewage treatment works and the sludge treatment centres would be required.

SLUDGE DISPOSAL STRATEGY AND THE BPEO

40. A review of international practice was carried out and future trends were considered. Agriculture, incineration and landfill have been regarded as the major disposal options but increasingly nations are looking at sludge as a resource from which to develop by-products, either to recycle to the land or for the production of usable materials. By the end of this decade technologies currently in the development stage may have been proven.

41. The requirement to stop the disposal of sludge at sea is resulting in a much greater demand for landfill capacity. This is being reduced by adopting incineration but with strict controls over air emission standards. Where agricultural land and forestry are available, the preference is to stabilize the sludge and then recycle it to these outlets because this is considered to be the best use of sludge.

42. The availability and capacity of sludge application to agricultural land was examined and it was shown that, theoretically, in many areas of the Region there is sufficient land to re-use the sludge arisings from local works. This is mainly in the rural areas of Lanark and Ayr, where at present there is some sludge re-use in agriculture. A nominal safety factor of ten times the available agricultural land necessary for sludge re-use was assumed in the evaluation, as the acceptance of sludge by farmers is not yet guaranteed.

43. Areas of forestry were also identified and the amounts of Forestry Commission, private woodland and areas for which planting grants have been approved, were quantified.

44. Within the urban areas of Strathclyde Region, large areas of derelict and vacant land have potential for reclamation. In and surrounding Glasgow

the Scottish Vacant Land Survey has identified over 4000ha of derelict and vacant land, about 35% (1400ha) of which is suitable for reclamation. There are also similar areas of land outside the Region but within reasonable transport distances.

45.　Notwithstanding the preference for re-use, a secure disposal route must also be available as a "back-up" option in the event of contamination of sludge or health risks concerning sludge use on agricultural land. Licensed contained landfill is available within the Glasgow area to meet this requirement. However, contained landfill also constitutes an alternative disposal strategy in its own right and, as such, has the potential for recovery of energy through production of methane gas and the generation of electricity.

46.　Re-use by the production of topsoil and construction products for sale is potentially valid, but at present the market for these products is limited. They cannot therefore be considered as main strategies, although serious consideration should be given to developing such markets.

47.　Four strategy options were developed for normal sewage works sludges, with the existing sea disposal method constituting Option No. 5. These options were evaluated and ranked in terms of environmental impact, operational security and cost.

48.　Essentially, Option No. 1 aims to re-use as much sludge as possible whilst providing secure back-up disposal to contained landfill.

49.　Contaminated raw sludge would be transported from individual sewage treatment works by road or pipeline to suitable treatment centres to be thickened, appropriately stabilised and dewatered. In cake form this would be transported to a contained landfill site for disposal. Once sludge contamination is brought under control by improved trade effluent control, the need for this disposal route will effectively disappear.

50.　Option No. 1, as shown in Fig. 6, emerged as the preferred option and it was concluded that it represents the BPEO for the Strathclyde Region.

51.　Having established the BPEO in terms of treatment, transport and disposal, this philosophy was then developed into a number of alternative engineering schemes.

SELECTION OF REGIONAL SCHEMES

52.　Practicable engineering schemes were developed which bring together the three elements of sludge disposal, treatment and transport.

53.　The Council's capital works programme for rationalisation of sewage treatment was taken into account. Just north of the City, the Kelvin Valley Sewerage Scheme has been designed to collect flows from thirteen sewage treatment works and transfer them to Dalmuir in the west. Dalmuir will then become the works requiring the largest capacity. It is to be reconstructed but the eventual location was not known at the time of the Study, and could conceivably have had an effect on the location of one of the proposed sludge treatment centres for the Glasgow conurbation. However it was assumed that at least the sewage treatment facilities will remain on the Dalmuir site, and this has now been confirmed. Daldowie has been developed to take the sewage from four other works and all other major schemes have been taken into account.

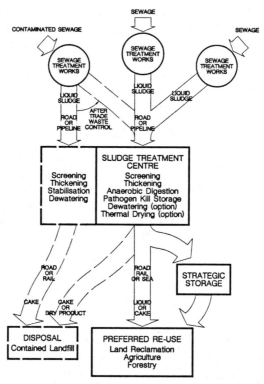

Fig. 6. Recommended strategy option

54. Development of engineering schemes was carried out in three phases, Glasgow conurbation (existing sea disposal catchment for sludge production), other mainland catchments, and island catchments.

55. Eight practicable schemes were identified to deal with sludge from the five principal sewage treatment works in the Glasgow conurbation (Shieldhall, Dalmuir, Paisley, Dalmarnock, Daldowie), which effectively comprise the existing sea disposal catchment. Four schemes were developed to cover the other mainland catchments, including those draining to the larger coastal towns such as Ayr. In total, 61 sources of sludge with population equivalents greater than 2 000 were incorporated into a number of alternative schemes. 28 of these had the potential to become treatment centres.

56. Schemes for the two mainland parts of the Region were blended together and five regional schemes were identified. These included two extreme solutions, involving practical maximum and minimum numbers of sludge treatment centres for the Region, and three other schemes which included variations to the numbers of centralised sludge treatment centres. The three schemes thus selected were considered in more detail in terms of

transport, operational security, environmental impact and cost.

57. In view of their special problems, remote mainland towns and those on the Islands were dealt with later.

58. Even though the estimated costs of the three schemes are virtually the same, the regional scheme shown in Fig. 7 was considered to represent the best alternative sludge treatment and disposal scheme for the Strathclyde Region.

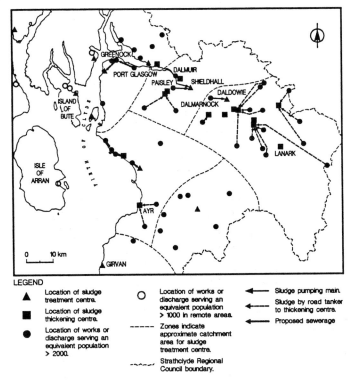

LEGEND

▲ Location of sludge treatment centre.

■ Location of sludge thickening centre.

● Location of works or discharge serving an equivalent population > 2000.

○ Location of works or discharge serving an equivalent population > 1000 in remote areas.

----- Zones indicate approximate catchment area for sludge treatment centre.

-·-·-·- Strathclyde Regional Council boundary.

◄── Sludge pumping main.

◄── Sludge by road tanker to thickening centre.

◄── Proposed sewerage

Fig. 7. Recommended regional scheme

EIA OF EXISTING MARINE DISPOSAL METHOD

59. The EIA of existing marine disposal of sludge in the Firth of Clyde, as shown in Fig. 2, was undertaken generally in accordance with the Environmental Assessment (Scotland) Regulations 1988. Investigations reviewed all existing data and attempted to identify the fate of the sludge particles. Following a scoping exercise, recommendations were made for fieldwork necessary to provide additional data on aspects of the disposal operation which had previously not been studied in sufficient detail.

60. A public consultation exercise aimed at identifying areas of general public concern was also undertaken and consultations were held with the appropriate statutory bodies.

61. Having collated and reviewed the available information, the significant issues and concerns were identified. This process established the scope of

the study, thereby providing a clear basis for the subsequent impact assessment and decision-making.

62.   Fieldwork was undertaken during stage two of the assessment. The data obtained were then analysed and interpreted and conclusions were formulated. Hitherto the present disposal site, with a depth of 70 to 90 metres, has been considered to be 'depositional,' with minimal dispersal by currents. As a result of the investigations it has been shown that up to 50% of the material disperses and does not settle directly to the bottom near the disposal site.

63.   The fact that raw sludge is disposed of to sea induces myriads of sea gulls to follow the sludge vessels. Recommendations were made which would improve the acceptability of the sea disposal operation. The most significant involves stabilisation of the sludge by digestion prior to disposal, since in this way the nature of the material would be changed and all floating organic material would be removed.

64.   The present method of disposal to sea does not represent best practice.

COMPARISON OF EXISTING AND THE BPEO

65.   The Terms of Reference called for a comparison to be made between the BPEO sludge strategy identified by the Study and the existing marine disposal method used for the sludge from the Glasgow area.

66.   A quantitative comparison of the Existing Marine Disposal Method and the Alternative, as identified by the BPEO methodology, was not feasible because of the very different environmental impacts. Such a comparison could also be considered as incorrect, since improvements to the existing method were identified during the Study and would have had to have been implemented should the existing method have been retained.

67.   However, from the studies carried out it has been possible to draw a number of conclusions about the Existing Method and the Alternative (the BPEO):

(i)   the Existing Marine Disposal is a relatively simple operation of benefit to the River Clyde and not normally affected by weather. The method leads to some enhancement of the local fisheries through the food chain. The MV Garroch Head carries passengers on several days each week during the summer months. This amenity is well used by the citizens of Strathclyde.

(ii)   the Existing Marine Disposal method has significant problems with odour at Shieldhall and Dalmuir sewage treatment works because it mostly involves raw sludge. Only about 50% of the sludge discharged is retained within the disposal area. Whilst the public health risk through the attendant seagulls is thought to be small, there is a potential risk to fishermen and yachtsmen from the surface slick. The effects of organochlorines and pathogens on the eco-system and up the food chain to man are unknown and it would be expensive to monitor this effectively.

(iii)   the Alternative Scheme will involve the digestion of all sludges, leading to a significant improvement in odour problems. Screening and digestion together will render the sludge less offensive than at present for disposal to land. Re-use of the sludge on land would be more controlled than at sea and easier to monitor. The BPEO allows for recovery of some energy through the digestion process and nutrients through the application to agricultural and other land.

(iv)   limitations on application seasons will require provision of strategic storage of sludge. The sludge treatment, transport and re-use/disposal operation will be more complex than the existing method and long-term impacts of sludge disposal to land will have to be kept under review.

68.   A number of improvements were identified which, if implemented, would make the existing marine disposal method more acceptable. These include:

(a)   improved trade effluent control of industrial sources;
(b)   thickening sludge to help confine it to the licensed disposal area on discharge;
(c)   improving loading facilities to reduce the odour problems;
(d)   fine screening to remove particulate matter;
(e)   stabilisation of sludges by digestion, thus reducing the surface slick, odour problems and potential health hazards and also deriving some energy before disposal.

IMPLEMENTATION OF THE RECOMMENDED SCHEME

69.   The Study concluded with suggestions for the implementation of the recommended scheme. These are considered under three headings: engineering requirements, programme, and costs.

70.   In order to arrive at closer cost estimates for the implementation of the necessary works, further estimates of the numbers and sizes of treatment units were made. These included for screening and thickening plant at 14 No. centres and sludge treatment and dewatering plant at 7 No. principal treatment centres, with sludge drying at Shieldhall and Daldowie sewage treatment works.

71.   The programme to meet the requirements of legislation has been developed in three phases. The operative dates are 1 January 1999, 2001 and 2006.

72.   The estimated capital costs of all of the works necessary to comply with the legislation is £100M. Estimated operational costs for the works are £6.2M per annum in 1999 rising to £8.8M per annum in 2006. Fig. 8 indicates the projected capital works expenditure profile for the recommended scheme.

RECOMMENDATIONS

73.   Twenty nine general and detailed recommendations were made. Twelve of these involving matters of principle are listed below:

(i)   Strenuous but realistic efforts continue to be made to improve the quality and nature of the sludge by stricter trade effluent control procedures.

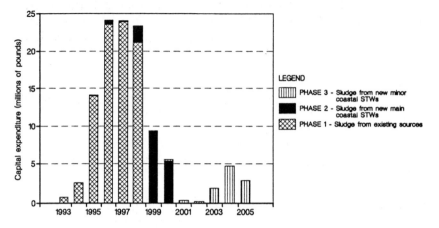

Fig. 8. Capital Expenditure Profile

(ii) Sludge disposal should involve the beneficial re-use of the product as far as is practicable.

(iii) Outlets should be developed for the re-use of sludge (principally in agriculture, forestry and land reclamation) and opportunities to develop other markets, for example in horticulture, should also be pursued.

(iv) Sludge which cannot be re-used in any of the normal outlets should be put in landfill sites in combination with domestic refuse.

(v) Sludge treatment should be based on stabilisation by mesophyllic anaerobic digestion, supplemented by thickening, dewatering and drying as required by the particular re-use outlets.

(vi) Individual sludges which remain, or are temporarily, contaminated to a degree which makes them unsuitable for re-use, should be treated by alkaline stabilisation and disposed of in a contained landfill.

(vii) Fine screening and thickening should be installed at all but the smallest sewage treatment works in order to improve the quality of the sludge and reduce the volumes and costs of sludge transport.

(viii) Road transport should remain the major means of transporting sludges to and from treatment centres.

(ix) Collection, thickening, treatment and disposal of sludge in the mainland area should be based on 14 No. sludge thickening centres and 7 No. sludge treatment centres.

(x) An appropriate management and operational structure should be established to develop and maintain the necessary sludge re-use outlets. This should include the monitoring and control of sludge and its impacts throughout the stages of production, storage, treatment, transport and disposal.

(xi) In remote mainland and island locations, mobile or transportable sludge thickening and dewatering equipment should be used.

(xii)   Depending upon the success of small scale reed bed sludge treatment, this method should be considered for future larger scale application, particularly in remote areas where population equivalents make digestion plants impracticable.

CONCLUDING REMARKS

74.   Strathclyde Regional Council are confident that they have adopted the most environmentally beneficial approach, and that sufficient outlets will be found to re-use all of the treated sludge.

75.   The availability of liquid, dewatered and dried biosolids products and the attendant progressive reductions in volume will allow flexibility in storage and transport.

76.   It is considered that sludge drying technology will continue to improve and so aid the development of new quality controlled biosolids products.

77.   Sufficient landfill capacity is available as a strategic back-up disposal route in Strathclyde.

78.   Incineration was shown to be unnecessary and offered no net advantage over the preferred outlets.

79.   The strategy is flexible and does not compromise the development of future product outlets. It is sustainable and regenerative in the widest sense.

80.   The strategy has been communicated to the public through a widely distributed brochure, advertising, and a series of public meetings, and has received general acceptance.

ACKNOWLEDGEMENTS

81.   The authors would like to take this opportunity to acknowledge the assistance of the many colleagues in both their own and other organisations who were involved in the Study. In particular it is appropriate to mention the Project Director Professor Alan Barrett of Montgomery Watson and Co-Director Clive Mason of Environmental Management Ltd., together with staff from Crouch Hogg Waterman. Professors George Fleming and Arthur Midwinter of Strathclyde University, and Professor James Bridges of the Robens Institute formed the Peer Review Group and are due a special note of thanks.

Quality requirements for sewage sludge now and into the future

J. E. HALL, BSc, WRc Medmenham, J. A. HOBSON, MA, MSc, WRc Swindon, and R. D. DAVIS, BSc, PhD, MIWEM, WRc Medmenham

SYNOPSIS. Sludge now has to be of high quality whatever the outlet selected for its disposal and this trend is likely to continue into the future. Clean sludge is compatible with any of the existing outlets which is the basis for a flexible and secure disposal operation. Also clean sludge provides the opportunity to develop marketable products for unrestricted use. Sludge quality is based on its biological, chemical and physical properties with the emphasis altering according to the outlet destined for the sludge. Sludge treatment needs to be determined according to quality requirements for the sludge which in turn depend on the planned disposal option.

LEGISLATION

1. Sewage sludge must be the most regulated waste in Europe with many EC Directives directly or indirectly affecting its production, treatment and disposal/reuse (see Fig. 1). Each country has to draw up legislation to implement these Directives (which can be made more stringent by Member States), but they may also have a range of other national regulations, codes of practice etc. Thus there are a wide range of standards and practices throughout Europe reflecting the differing environmental, operational, economic and political conditions in different countries, and their policies towards sludge disposal.

2. Waste management policy of the EC describes a hierarchy of waste disposal strategies: minimisation, recycling, incineration (energy recovery), landfilling. Current technology can do little to minimise sludge production, and in fact the Urban Waste Water Treatment (UWWT) Directive (ref. 1) will dramatically increase sludge production in Europe. Both the UWWT and the 'sludge to agriculture' Directive (ref. 2) state that sludge should be disposed of beneficially, but it is only in the latter Directive that there are any EC quality standards given for sludge reuse. Only one third of EC sludge is used beneficially on land (Table 1). For sludge disposed of by incineration and landfilling, which accounts for more than 60% of sludge production in the European Community, there are no quality limits as such set by the EC, although in practice, there are operational and environmental standards set by individual Member States. These normally relate to a minimum sludge dry solids content (for autothermic incineration, or landfill stability) and to emissions to the environment (flue gases, leachate etc).

double by 2005 but in some countries it will become technically, if not legally, impossible to use sludge in agriculture. This is due to differing policies in setting environmental quality standards, particularly with regard to heavy metals - apart from sludge treatment requirements to reduce odour and pathogen content, heavy metals are the principal target of all national regulations to avoid potential toxicity to plants, animals and man. For instance, a very conservative precautionary approach has been adopted in the Netherlands where the rate of addition of heavy metal contamination to soil must equal off-take by crops, whereas in the United States, permitted application rates and sludge qualities are very much higher, based on rigorous risk analysis to the most exposed individual (ref. 3-4). Table 2 shows the wide range of limit values between countries: the differences between some are up to two orders of magnitude.

4.   In the UK, the 'sludge to agriculture' Directive was implemented in 1989 by the Sludge (Use in Agriculture) Regulations (ref. 5) and by a National Code of Practice (ref. 6). No statutory limit values for heavy metals have been set for sludge since the UK (alone) adopted the alternative approach to controlling heavy metal additions permitted by the Directive where limits are based on the amount of metal applied per hectare (as opposed to limits on sludge quantity and dry solids addition). In the past this approach was seen as being flexible and pragmatic when sludges actually contained sufficient heavy metals to limit sludge use on land, however, over recent years pressures on industrial dischargers have dramatically reduced most of the heavy metal concentrations to the extent now that application rates of sludge are limited by the nutrient demand of the crop to be grown. Nevertheless, repeated applications of sludge, even 'clean' sludge will increase soil concentrations of heavy metals. The EC Directive 86/278 (ref. 2) sets a range of soil limit values within which Member States have set their own limits. Table 3 shows the wide range set by different countries.

5.   Whilst the limitation on crop nutrient demand is a general requirement of the EC Directive 86/218 (ref. 2), recent concerns over nitrate and phosphate emissions to surface and groundwater in Europe generally has resulted in the EC Directive on Nitrates (ref. 7), as well as various national measures to restrict nutrient additions to land. In the UK, limitations are currently non-statutory with a general blanket restriction of 250 kg N ha^{-1} from organic wastes such as sludge, applicable to all land, with much tighter restrictions in nitrate sensitive or vulnerable areas. There are no numerical limitations on phosphate in the UK but in some countries in Europe, these are set very low to avoid phosphate enrichment of soils, and so considerably restrict the amount of sludge that can be applied. This obviously increases land requirement and operational costs, and if permitted rates of application are set too low this will make sludge less attractive to farmers, particularly those who value its organic matter content more than the nutrients.

6.   Currently there is considerable interest in developing other beneficial and marketing outlets for sludge. Broadly these outlets are in commercial forestry, reclamation of derelict land and amenity uses (parks and gardens, green areas etc.) Not all countries in Europe permit sludge use in forests by law, but in the USA sludge is used extensively, and in the UK a manual of good practice has been

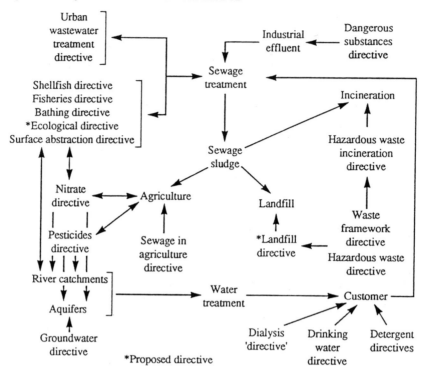

Fig. 1. The water directive cycle

Table 1. Current sludge disposal routes in the EC

	Quantities (t dry solids x 10^3)	Proportion (%)
Agriculture	1905	32
Landfill	2852	48
Incineration	784	13
Sea	301	5
Others	102	2
Total	5944	100

3.   With the pressure to recycle wastes, and with the increasing quantities of sludge for disposal in the UK due to the ending of sea disposal and the installation of treatment for sewage outfalls, much greater quantities of sludge will be used beneficially on land as an organic fertiliser. In the UK, the quantity recycled may

Table 2. Heavy metal limit values for sewage sludge in some countries (mg kg^{-1} dry solids)

	NL		D	CH	F	DK		S		EC	USA	
	Before 1995	After 1995				Before 1995	After 1995	Before 1995	After 1995		Clean sludge	Ceiling sludge
Zn	1400	300	2000/2500	2000	3000	4000	4000	1500	1500	2500-4000	2800	7500
Cu	425	75	800	600	1000	1000	1000	600	600	1000-1750	1500	4300
Ni	70	30	200	80	200	45	30	100	100	300-400	420	420
Cd	3.5	1.25	10/5	5	20	1.2	0.8	4	2	20-40	39	85
Pb	300	100	900	500	800	120	120	200	100	750-1200	300	840
Hg	3.5	0.75	8	5	10	1.2	0.8	5	2.5	16-25	17	57
Cr	350	75	1200	500	1000	100	100	150	150	1000-1500	1200	3000

Table 3. A comparison of present EC and UK and EC Member States maximum metal concentrations (mg kg^{-1} dry weight) in sludge amended soil

Element	EC[a]	UK[b]	Denmark	Germany	France	Italy	Netherlands[c]	Spain	USA[d]
Zinc	150 - 300	200 - 300[c]	100	200	300	300	84 - 240	150	1500
Copper	50 - 140	80 - 135[e]	40	60	100	100	23 - 55	50	775
Nickel	30 - 75	50 - 75[e]	15	50	50	50	20 - 70	30	230
Cadmium	1 - 3	3	0.5	1.5	2	3	0.5 - 1.0	1	20
Lead	50 - 300	300	40	100	100	100	63 - 117	50	190
Mercury	1 - 1.5	1	0.5	1	1	-	-	1	9
Chromium	[100 - 150][f]	400[g]	30	100	150	150	70 - 170	100	1540

Notes: (a) Limits from EEC 1986 (ref. 2)
(b) Limit from DoE 1989 (ref. 5-6)
(c) Depending on soil type
(d) Approximate value calculated from US EPA 1993
(e) According to soil pH (ref. 5-6)
(f) Provisional - now withdrawn
(g) Limit from DoE 1989

Table 4. Current and proposed limit values for heavy metals in composts (mg kg ds^{-1})

	Austria			Belgium			Denmark	France AFNOR	Germany				Italy	
	ONorm S-2022	ONorm Class 1	S-2200 Class 2	Agric.	Park	VFG proposed			Blue Angel	BGGK	RAL	Current	A proposed	B proposed
Zn	1000	210	400	1000	1500	280	4000 [1]	-	300	400	400	2500	400	1500
Cu	400	70	100	100	500	90	1000 [1]	-	75	100	100	600	200	500
Ni	100	42	60	50	100	20	45	200	50	50	50	200	50	200
Cd	4	0.7	1	5	5	1	1.2	8	1	2	1.5	10	3	5
Pb	500	70	150	600	1000	120	120 [2]	800	100	150	150	500	200	600
Hg	4	0.7	1	5	5	0.7	1.2	8	1	1.5	1	10	2	5
Cr	150	70	70	150	200	70	100 [1]	-	100	100	100	500/100 [3]	150	500

Table 4 continued

	The Netherlands				Spain	Switzerland		UK
	To end 1994	Clean to end 1994	From 1995	Clean from 1995		Current	Proposed	UKROFS[4]
Zn	900	280	200	75	4000	500	400	1000
Cu	300	90	60	25	1750	150	100	400
Ni	50	20	20	10	400	50	30	100
Cd	2	1	1	0.7	40	3	1	10
Pb	200	120	100	65	1200	150	120	250
Hg	2	0.7	0.3	0.2	25	3	1	2
Cr	200	70	50	50	750	150	100	1000

1 containing sewage sludge
2 80 mg kg ds^{-1} in private garden
3 Cr III/Cr IV
4 manure for organic farming

developed by WRc and the forestry Authority (ref. 8). For sludge use in land reclamation, a draft code of practice has been produced in the UK by WRc (ref. 9), but there is no direct legislation for this outlet in Europe.

7.   For amenity uses in particular, but also increasingly for other recycling outlets, it is recognised that conventional liquid or dewatered sludges are not the most attractive or marketable products. Attention has recently focused on treatment processes such as composting, thermal drying and N-viro (lime treatment) to produce more readily 'marketable' products. However, legislation in the UK is not clear as to whether such products are still sludge and how their use should be controlled. a recent WRc study on this issue concluded that this ambiguity was actually inhibiting to the wider adoption of such processes and products (ref. 10). In many countries in Europe, there is specific legislation for composts, whilst in others it is integrated with other sludge legislation and forms a unified set of standards for all types of organic waste derived products. However, many of the standards for composts in Europe would exclude sludge unless it formed only a small component of the product due to the very stringent heavy metal limits adopted by some countries (see Table 4). There is currently a European Standards committee (CEN 223) considering soil improvers and growing media, and it is hoped that this will take a pragmatic and flexible approach to setting safety standards, although early indications suggest that this may aim to set levels so low as to permit uncontrolled use. This would appear to be unnecessarily restrictive since in the United States considerable amounts of sludge and sludge products are sold for domestic gardens provided they meet the standards set by their risk assessment (see Table 2).

SLUDGE QUALITY

8.   Sludge quality is based on its biological, chemical and physical properties with the emphasis altering according to the outlet destined for the sludge. Biological properties include the microbiological stability of the organic matter in the sludge, odour and infectivity. Sludge treatment processes have an important effect on the biological quality of sludge and stabilisation processes such as mesophilic anaerobic digestion improve all three characteristics by stabilising the organic matter and reducing odour potential and numbers and infectivity of pathogenic micro-organisms. Descriptions of processes which satisfactorily stabilise sludge prior to its use in agriculture are described in the DoE Code of Practice (ref. 6). Heat-dried sludge should also achieve good biological quality. Full pasteurisation is not usually practised in the UK. Pasteurised sludge is not necessarily microbiologically stable and it represents a medium for recolonisation by pathogenic micro-organisms. Chemical properties include content of metals, other potentially toxic elements and organic contaminants and concentrations and availability of plant nutrients. As discussed below, sludge treatment processes have little effect on metals and refractive organic compounds but may facilitate the breakdown of degradable organics and can substantially alter the plant nutrient content of sludge and availability to crops after application to land. By degrading part of the sludge solids content anaerobic digestion increases the concentration of metals in sludge expressed on a dry solids basis. Control over the content and form of nitrogen in sludge to be

recycled is important both to comply with regulations and to ensure that the crop response to sludge meets the farmer's expectations. Physical properties include whether solid or liquid (extent of thickening and dewatering) and aesthetic factors associated for instance with removal of unsightly debris by effective screening. The physical quality of sludge can be controlled by appropriate treatment.

THE CHEMICAL QUALITY OF SLUDGE

9.   During sewage treatment a high proportion of the contaminants such as heavy metals in the incoming wastewater are transferred by processes such as precipitation and adsorption into the sludge. Organic contaminants in sludge include detergent-based compounds such as linear alkylbenzene sulphonate and compounds that are widely used by industry or in the home. During sludge treatment organic contaminants are either conserved, volatilized, degraded or produced. Generally the physico-chemical properties which favour incorporation of organic compounds into sewage sludge also favour conservation during sludge treatment. Data on the percentage removal of metals during primary and secondary sewage treatment are given in Table 5. The removal of metals is advantageous with respect to the quality of sewage effluent for discharge to the receiving water. But it results in concentrations of metals in the sludge for disposal which may be >1000 x higher (mg kg^{-1} dry solids basis) than in the original wastewater (mg l^{-1} basis). Thus even comparatively low concentrations of metals in wastewater may affect the quality of sludge and its suitability for disposal since there are statutory limits for metals in sludge-treated soils. In this context the elements of most interest have been the comparatively bioavailable heavy metals such as zinc, copper, nickel and cadmium. There are statutory limits also for mercury and lead and in the UK there are additional limits for chromium, molybdenum, selenium, arsenic and fluoride. Access to beneficial recycling opportunities requires sludge of low metal content and with this in mind industrial discharges to the sewer have been progressively restricted to protect the quality of sludge for disposal. Table 6 compares sludge quality in 1982/83 and 1990/91. It is seen that during this period the median concentrations of zinc, copper, nickel and chromium in sludge have decreased by approximately one third, lead by half and cadmium by two-thirds. For most sludges there is little or no scope to improve quality further by restrictions on industrial discharges. Looking to the future the limiting elements are likely to be zinc and copper because of their widespread use in household products particularly pharmaceuticals (zinc) and plumbing (copper). Approximately 30% of the lead in domestic sludge comes via runoff from aerial deposition and the lower lead concentrations in the 1990/91 survey may already reflect declining use of leaded petrol. Industrial and other uses of mercury and cadmium are closely controlled.

212

Table 5. Percentage of metals removed from sewage during primary and secondary sewage treatment and transferred into sewage sludge

Metal	Cd	Cr	Cu	Ni	Pb	Zn
Primary	59	40	54	19	72	48
Secondary	29	33	36	25	21	30
Total	88	73	90	44	93	78

Table 6. Median concentrations of metals (mg kg^{-1} ds) in UK sewage sludge utilised on agricultural land (ref. 11-12)

Element	1982/83	1990/91
Zinc	1205	889
Copper	625	473
Nickel	59	37
Cadmium	9	3
Lead	418	217
Mercury	3	3
Chromium	124	86
Molybdenum	5	1
Selenium	3	0.3
Arsenic	5	3

USE OF TREATMENT PROCESSES TO CONTROL SLUDGE QUALITY

10. Before moving onto a brief overview of what processes are available for cleaning sludge and what levels of cleanliness can be obtained, it must be emphasized that processes themselves have environmental impacts over and above those of their products. These impacts stem from, amongst others, the land occupied by the process, the energy and raw materials used by the process, by-products from the process and the transport required to move materials to and from the process. The impacts are not always local to the process, e.g. the main impact from using electricity is at the power station where it was generated. Some impacts are positive. Anaerobic digestion produces methane which may be used to generate electricity, thus reducing the environmental impact otherwise resulting from its generation. In a similar way the value of the N and P content of sewage sludge and derived products when used in agriculture can be estimated from the energy saved in the manufacture of energy intensive inorganic fertilisers. Disposal or re-use options must therefore be evaluated together with all of the processes employed. Fig. 2 shows the inputs, outputs and impacts of a treatment process where the outlet is agricultural re-use.

213

What we are talking about are in fact some of the considerations that go into the selection of the best practicable environmental option, known as the BPEO. Procedures for the selection of the BPEO have been recommended by the Royal Commission on Environmental Pollution in its 12th report (ref. 13) for large schemes which have a significant environmental impact. In addition, WRc, on behalf of Her Majesty's Inspectorate of Pollution has further developed these procedures specifically for use in deciding between sludge disposal options (ref. 14). Parameters of significance when selecting a BPEO include traffic generation, emission of acid and greenhouse gases and net primary energy (NPE). This latter term is the sum over the selected lifetime of the project of all of the energy inputs and outputs, reduced to a common form, namely equivalent tonnes of coal. NPE includes the energy required to produce all of the raw materials, including those of construction, consumed by the process and can sometimes be negative due to the production of digester gas and the replacement of inorganic fertilisers. Such negative NPE terms will also have associated negative productions of acid and greenhouse gases, most of which derive from the production of energy.

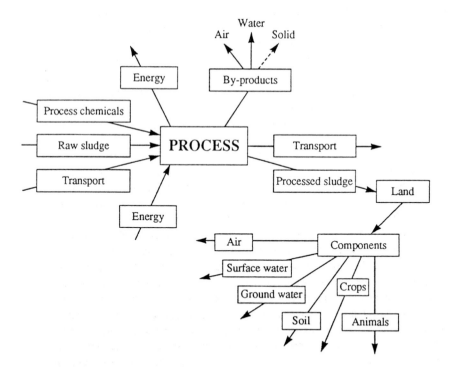

Fig. 2. Sludge treatment process inputs, outputs and impacts for agriculture

11. Moving onto processes themselves, there are a number of issues, as discussed above, that need or may need to be addressed in order to produce a 'clean' sludge.

* Water content
* Contamination by aesthetically unacceptable debris
* Stabilization
* Odour
* Bacterial and other pathogen content
* Metal content
* Nitrogen and phosphorus content
* Content of trace organic compounds

Water content

12. Considered in isolation the statement that the water content and quality of sludges are inversely related is difficult to contradict. However it has already been shown that the quality of sludge or sludge products should not be considered in isolation. When the energy required for dewatering or drying is considered together with the potential loss of valuable components from the sludge during dewatering, the use of liquid sludge in agriculture can still be a strong candidate for the BPEO. Nevertheless there are several good reasons for reducing the water content of sewage sludge; many downstream processes become more economic or more efficient, the costs and impacts of subsequent transport are greatly reduced, the aesthetic appearance of the product is improved particularly by drying, much odour is lost in the dewatering process and finally, drying both pasteurises the sludge and by virtue of the low water content of the final product, prevents regrowth of organisms.

13. Processes for water removal start with gravity thickening, which typically raises the solids content of sludge from 2-4% to 5-10%. Biological activity which leads to gas production in the thickener can be deleterious and there is a tendency towards using the process for primary sludges only. Secondary sludges can be thickened on a belt thickener employing the addition of polyelectrolytes. They may also be thickened by dissolved air flotation (DAF) and the possibility of bioflotation has recently been raised. Centrifuges can be used for thickening as well as dewatering to a solids content in the range 25-35%. The latter can also be achieved by belt presses, drum filters and filter presses, all employing the addition of polyelectrolytes. Drying to produce a solids content of from 70-95% depending on the process and the intended application of the sludge, can take place in a range of modern equipment including rotary drum dryers employing direct or indirect heating or in fluidised bed dryers. By a combination of condensing drying vapours and recycling them and routing excess vapour back to the combustion process which provides heat, most odour is contained within the process unlike some older sludge drying systems which received a very bad reputation for causing a smell nuisance.

Contamination by aesthetically unacceptable debris

14. UK sewage works typically screen crude sewage using 1" bar screens, though there is a growing trend towards fine screening employing 6 mm openings. The former are not sufficient to prevent all unsightly debris from reaching the sludge and

at some works sludge screens are employed. It can be assumed that fine screening of crude sewage will eliminate the need for sludge screens. It is important that sludges imported from small works and septic tanks are also adequately screened.

Stabilization

15. The major purpose of stabilisation is to improve sludge aesthetically. There are in fact several definitions of 'stabilised' as applied to sewage sludge. The most fundamental is the destruction of fermentable organic material, typically in a biological digestion process. Such destruction would generally represent 40-50% of the volatile matter originally present in the sludge. Sludges which have been altered in some way to prevent fermentation, such as by lime or calcium oxide addition or drying, can also be considered stabilised. In these cases stabilisation may only be temporary since conditions could change again so as to allow fermentation. Finally any sludge which is relatively odour-free could be considered as stabilised. Four potential biological stabilisation processes exist as shown in Table 7.

Table 7. Most common types of biological stabilisation processes.

	Aerobic	Anaerobic
Liquid sludge	Thermophilic Aerobic Digestion (TAD)	Mesophilic Anaerobic Digestion
Dewatered sludge	Composting	Processes exist for other substrates but not developed for sewage sludge

Odour

16. All of these biological stabilisation processes significantly reduce the odour released from the product to a level acceptable for most agricultural practices, although only composting is likely to produce a totally aesthetically acceptable product. Chemical stabilisation with lime or calcium oxide does not destroy odours but fixes many of the most unpleasant compounds in a non-volatile state, again resulting in a product acceptable for most agricultural practices. When combined with de-watering, much ammonia is lost both to the water and via direct volatilisation to the air resulting in a further reduction in odour. Drying removes most of the odorous compounds present but if the sludge has not previously been stabilised, re-wetting can initiate new fermentation and the production of further odour. Other chemical treatments can reduce odours from sludge. Hydrogen sulphide can be fixed as non-volatile iron sulphide by the addition of iron salts. The addition of strong oxidants can significantly reduce sludge odours, though this is very costly. One of the most effective is sodium chlorite which can make a significant improvement which lasts for up to 2 days, perhaps enough to allow the application of an unstabilised liquid sludge to land.

Bacterial and other pathogen content

17. The bacterial and pathogen content of sludges can be reduced by thermal or chemical means. Pasteurisation can be brought about by holding sludge at at least 70 °C for at least 30 minutes. Heating can be brought about by conventional hot water heat exchangers or by submerged combustion, where gases are combusted within the sludge or by the bubbling of hot gases from an external combustor through the sludge. Biothermal processes can also pasteurise if sludge can be maintained above 55 °C for at least 4 hours. Both the aerobic processes, TAD and composting, can achieve this. In all of these processes a very small degree of short-circuiting or contamination of product by untreated sludge can hugely compromise the levels of pathogen reduction. Raising pH levels to 12 by the addition of lime (or calcium oxide to dewatered sludge, when heat is also released) brings about adequate disinfection. Reduction of pH values by the addition of acid can also bring about disinfection, though no processes exist expressly for this purpose.

Metal content

18. Nearly all sludge disposal routes are affected by one or other of the regulations or codes concerning heavy metals, as discussed above, and reductions in their levels would be highly desirable. Most work on metals reduction has revolved around acid leaching. However this has generally been considered unacceptably costly for the acid required and then the alkali to bring the pH value of the product back to neutrality. Performance is also variable. Holding sludge at pH 1.5 for 24 hours results in from 20-80% reductions depending to some extent on the type of sludge but more particularly on the metal species; zinc showing good removals, copper less so. Removal rates can be enhanced by the addition of strong oxidising agents or complexing agents but these increase the costs even further. More recently some advance seems to have been made using bio-leaching. Here sludge is enriched with sulphur and aerated for up to 5 days. Sulphur bacteria oxidise the sulphur to sulphuric acid *in-situ* producing pH values down to 1.5 (iron oxidising bacteria can also play a role). Since sulphur is cheaper than sulphuric acid, significant savings are made and it appears the percentage reductions in metal levels are significantly better than simple acid leaching. To date no economically viable process has been demonstrated. WRc is currently working on an integrated bio-leaching process, for which a patent has been applied for. The acid for leaching is both created and destroyed biologically in a cyclic process. Hydrogen sulphide is produced by the biochemical reaction between sludge and sulphate in a digester, according to Equation 1 (where CH_2O approximates to sludge). Such a digester destroys sulphuric acid and simultaneously oxidises (stabilises) the sludge.

$$H_2SO_4 + 2CH_2O = 2CO_2 + 2H_2O + H_2S \tag{1}$$

The hydrogen sulphide produced can be collected and oxidised to sulphuric acid in a bioscrubber according to Equation 2.

$$H_2S + 2O_2 = H_2SO_4 \tag{2}$$

The acid may be used for metal leaching, with a portion of the H_2S used to precipitate the metals in the leachate for separation, before being returned to the digestion step. In this way sludge is both stabilised as well as reduced in metal content. If Equations 1 and 2 are added it can be seen that the sulphate is only cycled catalytically while sludge solids are oxidised. All three of the leaching processes also disinfect the sludge. So far only the individual steps of this scheme have been studied, although WRc hopes to shortly construct an integrated pilot plant.

Nitrogen and phosphorus content

19. The nitrogen and phosphorus content of sewage sludge is generally considered beneficial for its fertilizer value, though the impact of the recently introduced nitrogen limits on land, discussed above, may on occasions favour sludge with a lower nitrogen content. There is some scope for reductions in the nitrogen load associated with sludge. Most nitrogen in raw sludge is organically bound. During the various digestion processes, from 33-50% of this nitrogen is mineralised to form ammonia. In any subsequent dewatering step, this ammonia is removed from the sludge and generally recycled through the sewage works. Unfortunately, ammonia is the fraction of the nitrogen content that is most desired by farmers. Phosphorus is little affected by most treatment processes. Where phosphorus removal is employed at a sewage works, if by chemical means, the sludge can be significantly enriched in phosphorus. Biological phosphorus removal also generally leads to enhanced phosphorus levels in the raw sludge. In this case, though, digestion resolubilises much of this additional phosphorus, which would therefore be lost along with ammonia in any subsequent dewatering step. Where sludges of very high quality are to be produced, consideration has been given to enriching them with inorganic fertiliser to make them more attractive to potential users.

Content of trace organic compounds

20. In recent years there has been considerable interest in what happens to specific organic compounds during sewage treatment, and a number of 'fate' models have been developed to predict this. Generally such models predict what percentage of an organic compound in the incoming sewage ends up in the raw sludge. For many compounds this percentage can be high. Rather less attention has been paid as to the subsequent fate of such compounds in sludge. Digestion processes remove a large percentage of the more degradable compounds, while the more volatile material can be transferred into the gas phase. There are though many refactory compounds, frequently chlorinated organics of solely man-made origin, which are not significantly removed in the currently available processes, save for incineration and other processes which totally destroy the sludge fabric. In the absence of processes to reliably reduce levels of trace organic compounds attention is shifting to determine their long term fate after application to soil. Even a very slow rate of destruction, as the sludge is fully mineralized in the soil, would be sufficient to ensure there is no long term build-up of such compounds.

21. It can be seen that many processes exist, both established and experimental, for improving the quality of sludge to a sufficient level for many applications. There is still some way to go before the development of processes to economically produce a totally clean sludge.

REFERENCES
1. CEC; Commission of the European Communities. Council Directive of 21 May 1991 concerning urban waste water treatment (91/271/EEC). Official Journal of the European Communities, 1991, No. L 135/40-52.

2. CEC; Commission of the European Communities. Council Directive of 12 June 1986 on the protection of the environment, and in particular of the soil, when sewage sludge is used in agriculture (86/278/EEC). Official Journal of the European Communities, 1986, No. L 181/6-12.

3. US EPA; US Environmental Protection Agency. Development of Risk Assessment Methodology for Land Application and Distribution and Marketing of Municipal Sludge. EPA 600/6-89/001. (1989). National Technical Information Service, Springfield VA.

4. US EPA; US Environmental Protection Agency. Part 503-Standards for the Use or Disposal of Sewage Sludge. Federal Register, 58, 9387-9404, 1993.

5. SI; UK Statutory Instrument. The Sludge (Use in Agriculture) Regulations. Statutory Instrument No. 1263. 1989, HMSO, London.

6. DoE; Department of the Environment. Code of Practice for Agricultural Use of Sludge, 1989, HMSO, London.

7. CEC; Commission of the European Communities. Council Directive of 12 December 1991 concerning the protection of waters against pollution caused by nitrates from agricultural sources (91/676/EEC). Official Journal of the European Communities, 1991, No. L 375/1-8.

8. WOLSTENHOLME, R., DUTCH, J., BAYES, C.D. and TAYLOR, C.M.A. A manual of good practice for the use of sewage sludge in forestry. Bulletin 107, 1992, HMSO.

9. HALL, J.E. The use of sewage sludge in land restoration. Draft Code of Practice. WRc Report ER 1345-M, 1989.

10. HALL, J.E. Alternative uses of sewage sludge for land application. WRc Report DoE 3357(P), 1993.

11. SLEEMAN, P.J. and DAVIS, R.D. Multi-element analysis of the trace element contents of UK sewage sludges in 1982/83. WRc Medmenham Report DoE 280-S(P), 1991.

12. DEPARTMENT OF THE ENVIRONMENT, UK. Sewage Sludge Survey, Final Report, 1993.

13. ROYAL COMMISSION ON ENVIRONMENTAL POLLUTION 12th Report. Best Practicable Environmental Option. Her Majesty's Stationery Office, London, 1988 (Cmnd 310).

14. POWLESLAND, C. and FROST, R. C. WRc, Medmenham, 1990, Report DoE 2305-M/1.

Poster papers

The following poster papers were presented at Water Environment '94.

Fishery measures in Northern Ireland with particular reference to the River Blackwater Fishery Rehabilitation Scheme

N. N. J. HIGGINSON, BSc, MSc, PhD, CEng, MICE, Senior Engineer, Department of Agriculture for Northern Ireland

Dover and Folkestone wastewater treatment project

EurIng D. V. ROGERS, BSc, CEng, MICE, MIWEM, Deputy Managing Director, Coastal Wastewater Consultants Ltd

Fluidised bed sludge incineration

D. J. LAX, PhD, MICE, MIWEM, Divisional Manager, Taylor Woodrow

International experience in the design of nutrient removal plants to meet the Urban Wastewater Treatment Directive

A. V. GRAY, BSc, PhD, CChem, FRSC, MIWEM, Principal Process Chemist, Montgomery Watson Ltd

Total nitrogen removal from a heavily polluted rendering plant wastewater

E. DOBOLYI, MS(ChemEng), MS(SanitEng), Chief Scientist, Treatwater International Ltd

Reconstruction and upgrading of small community sewage treatment works (Thames Water — Key Change Programme 3)

J. LONGSTAFF, CEng, MICE, MAPM, Project Manager, Howard Humphreys & Partners

Catchment planning for wastewater management

T. J. TURPIN, BSc, MSc, MInstWM, FIWEM, Director, Nicholas Pearson Associates Ltd

'Operation Seaclean' — an environmental achievement for Southern Water

R. CLAYTON, DMS, CEng, MICE, MIStructE, MIWEM, Technical Director, and J. BIRCUMSHAW, BSc, CEng, MICE, Planning Manager, Southern Water Services Ltd